D0193536

"You're blushing like a rose," Devin said

His expression was mocking, but teasing, as well.

"It's something about you that does it," Susan risked everything and told the truth.

"Do you think I don't know it?" Devin looked at her with no surprise on his face. "You're not falling in love with me, are you?" He made it sound the ultimate in stupidity.

"No." A dreamlike sensitivity was overtaking her. She leaned her head against his chest. "I know you never believed me, but I did dream about you in the forest."

"Did you dream I made love to you?" he asked tauntingly. His hands slid down and tightened around her waist, drawing her to him. "You could have. I find you beautiful...the most innocent little witch in the world."

Other titles by
MARGARET WAY
IN HARLEQUIN ROMANCES

Other titles by
MARGARET WAY
IN HARLEQUIN PRESENTS

Many of these titles are available at your local bookseller.

For a free catalogue listing all available Harlequin Romances,
send your name and address to:

HARLEQUIN READER SERVICE,
M.P.O. Box 707, Niagara Falls, N.Y. 14302
Canadian address: Stratford, Ontario, Canada N5A 6W2

Blue Lotus

by

MARGARET WAY

Harlequin Books

TORONTO • LONDON • NEW YORK • AMSTERDAM
SYDNEY • HAMBURG • PARIS • STOCKHOLM

Original hardcover edition published in 1979
by Mills & Boon Limited

ISBN 0-373-02328-6

Harlequin edition published April 1980

Copyright © 1979 by Margaret Way.
Philippine copyright 1979. Australian copyright 1979.

All rights reserved. Except for use in any review, the reproduction or utilization
of this work in whole or in part in any form by any electronic, mechanical or
other means, now known or hereafter invented, including xerography,
photocopying and recording, or in any information storage or retrieval system,
is forbidden without the permission of the publisher. All the characters in this
book have no existence outside the imagination of the author and have no
relation whatsoever to anyone bearing the same name or names. They are not
even distantly inspired by any individual known or unknown to the author, and
all the incidents are pure invention.

The Harlequin trademark, consisting of the word HARLEQUIN and the
portrayal of a Harlequin, is registered in the United States Patent Office and in
the Canada Trade Marks Office.

Printed in U.S.A.

CHAPTER ONE

IT was her third day alone and she was incredibly thirsty. The heat of the sun was scorching and there was a curious, melting feeling right through her body. She didn't know how far she had wandered since Jeff had left her. She could even be going around in circles, though she had never found her way back to their battered, broken-down Land Rover. It had carried them safely over thousands of miles, now it was stranded somewhere back there in the great wilderness with a broken axle. Jeff should never have made that semi-facetious remark about what a damned nuisance it would be to break down in the jungle. Less than an hour later, with Sue jolted sick beside her brother, they had ground out of thick vegetation to come down on a hidden rocky gully, where they had stayed until Jeff had gone off for help. That was Day One.

Mid-morning of the second day, Susan had decided to go after her brother, frightened if she stayed in the one place, the steamy tropical rain forest would envelop her and they would never find her again. She had been in a state of fear and minor agony ever since then. Last night the mosquitoes had ravished her tender skin, and when she awoke to a deafening chorus of screeching and warbling and twittering, a large brown snake with a yellow underbelly was coiled around the lowest branch of a flowering melaleuca directly above

5

her. She had started up at once, the shrill involuntary cry that pealed up from her throat scattering the parrots that flashed brilliant enamel colours through the dense green of the bush.

It was strange to be lost, though people got lost in the bush all the time. Up until now, their trip had been wonderful, a great change and a challenge for the twenty-two-year-old Susan. Hers had been a quiet, sheltered life, not altogether happy. Ever since their mother had died when Susan was twelve and Jeff fourteen, she had tried to take her mother's place, looking after the house, and caring for her father and brother. Between them they had managed and after the terrible shock of their grief had worn off, there was still happiness and security in their home; a caring and sharing. It had lasted for two years, with Susan and Jeff certain that nothing could come between them and their father, but Charles Blake was not by nature a man who could live without the love and comfort of a woman. It wasn't too late for him to start again so at the age of forty-two he found himself another wife.

Pamela, their stepmother, had stripped them of all their security. She was attractive and clever and genuinely in love with her husband, but she had never had the slightest desire to care for his children. For years she had worked as Charles Blake's secretary and she had been secretly in love with him for most of that time. Then came the news of Lisa Blake's sudden tragic death, and from that moment on Pamela had done everything in her power to make herself indispensable to Charles. He was exactly the sort of man she had always wanted, but she had no intention of rearing his children. Children were too demanding and their demands were certain to conflict with her own personal needs.

Jeff had been glad to go off to boarding school, but Charles, who couldn't really fathom what was going on in his own home, refused point blank to let his beloved little daughter out of his sight. Jeff had come to the difficult age and the discipline of boarding school would do him good, but Susan was so lovely, so sweet and sensitive and comforting, he had refused to go along with what were really Pamela's plans. The pressures of his business made him leave a lot of the decisions to her, but his devotion to his children was very real and he was especially protective of his daughter.

Pamela, to do her justice, wasn't unkind, but what warmth was in her she kept for her husband. Susan quickly came to accept the fact her stepmother simply lacked the temperament and the deep womanly generosity to take to another woman's child. The years passed with both Susan and Jeff lacking for nothing except the love and understanding they had once known. Pamela, right up until the time Susan had left home, had remained a stranger, deeply resentful of the fact that she had been unable to give her husband their own child, tolerating Susan because after all she did have good manners, but actively hostile to the much more aggressive Jeff, who now had an apartment of his own and only visited his father every other weekend. Both Susan and Jeff had received an excellent education and Pamela reasoned that they should stand on their own two feet instead of relying on their father for comfort and closeness. How else would they learn self-reliance?

She had been so clever about it, Charles Blake came

to believe it was his duty to let Susan take a place of her own as soon as she turned twenty-one, though his concern showed itself in the way he insisted on finding her a suitable apartment in the right area and helping out with a monthly cheque. Pamela had pointed out to him that he was too possessive of his daughter, but the thought didn't fill him with guilt. His daughter was all he had to remind him of Lisa. Young people seemed to need space of their own, though Charles Blake truly believed a daughter should remain at home until the day she married. It was the best place for an innocent young girl, and Susan was so beautiful she looked as if she needed protection.

Susan, in fact, was very sensible and competent, but she had still allowed herself to be talked into this escape to freedom, to the adventure they had never known. Jeff was very persuasive and he decided after a hard year of saving that they should take time off to recover from the long years under Pamela's régime. Susan had been granted special leave of absence from the Education Department who employed her as a teacher and Jeff had given up a 'go nowhere job', as he called it, in favour of going exactly where he liked. He and Susan had always lived together in perfect accord and Jeff certainly thought Susan deserved a break. He had been out from under Pamela's feet for long periods at a time, but Susan had borne the full brunt of being treated like a boarder in her own home. Susan was like their mother—that was the trouble. Pamela had never enjoyed hearing the resemblance pointed out, for under that cool, sophisticated exterior, she was violently jealous. Susan herself hardly dared dwell on the isolated occasions Pamela had shown it. No one would believe her anyway, except Jeff. Mercifully their father was blind to Pamela's faults, since she was a very in-control lady whenever he was about.

If Pamela could only see her now! Susan stood clinging motionless to the frond of a great fern that soared twenty and more feet into the air. She would have to fight out of this continuous tree canopy and into the open woodland. Jeff would never find his way back to her. Birdsong was carrying far through the air and despite her fears and anxieties she felt intensely distracted. Many of the trees were in fruit and flower and she could hear the heavy flapping of wings. Even on the ground the search for food was frenzied with insects and lizards darting through the thick carpet of fallen casuarina needles.

Thick woody vines crisscrossed the path ahead. The mosses, the giant tree ferns, the beautiful flowering orchids told her she was moving further into the rain forest instead of out of it. Here the trees' overgreen crowns interlocked and the plant life became even more overwhelming. The fan palms were on a gigantic scale and every available inch was saturated with plant life. It seemed incredible to have come from the savage lonely beauty of the Inland, the endless open plains, to the luxuriant rugged North. Capricornia was another world, in stunning contrast to the Dead Heart. Not that it was dead, for they had seen it in a lucky good season when wildflowers sprang up in their millions to dazzle the eye and take one's breath away with their endless profusion.

Australia was such a vast, unexpected continent, and up until now they had seen very little of it beyond the crowded cities. The ten-million-acre Heartland had been superb; a bizarre fantasyland of towering blood-red sandhills; the splendid isolation of Ayers Rock and the extraordinary brilliance of its colour displays; the winter weather glorious. Now Susan was on fire with her walk through the jungle. The reason they had come North was to see all the lush beauty tropical Queensland had to offer—the eternal miles of sugar cane, the cattle kingdoms. She had loved it so much, their wandering in the wilds. They had even discussed the idea of going across to one of the Great Barrier Reef islands. Perhaps Heron, a true coral atoll. The Reef, a great natural wonder of the world, started below Capricorn and ribboned its way north over thirteen hundred miles, a great coral rampart twenty miles wide. Susan had never seen any of the hundreds of islands, but they were supposed to be breathtakingly beautiful. Jeff had planned to go scuba diving. Right now she would give anything for the sight of the unbelievably blue water they had glimpsed along the coast road.

The day wore on, so hot she had to keep her movements to a minimum. A strange little sound of desolation reached her ears and only gradually did she become aware that it was the sound of her own weeping. Jeff wasn't going to find her. No one was going to find her. Here in this terrestrial paradise with bracts of orchids cascading six feet down the trees she was going to die.

Pictures began flashing themselves across her mind. The image of her mother laughing. How beautiful she had been! How loving and kind and funny. Before their father had married Pamela he had taken both of his children into his confidence, explaining how difficult it was for him to live without the loving support of a wife even if he knew he would never find again the perfect companion, the beloved woman, their mother. In her mind's eye she could see all her family as they had been, the fun they had had, the happy times.... From weeping she now seemed to be laughing weakly and she wondered if it was the effect of the berries she had eaten. They had to be all right, for the birds were eating them.

She couldn't bear the thought of night falling, the whispering jungle, the inky darkness under the trees. She was desperately worried about Jeff. Where was he? He would never abandon her, so it seemed likely that he too had become lost. It was easy, so easy in this velvet green gloom. The sight of the great lawyer vines was frightening her. They were hanging down like gigantic ropes or twining themselves around the forest giants, so she was forced to travel with fearful slowness. To give herself a little courage she picked the scented flower of a cascading orchid and thrust it through the buttonhole of her torn and stained cotton shirt. She was extremely sensitive to beauty and the action was characteristic of her even in her badly distressed state.

Later she came on wild banana and sat down before the flying buttresses of a giant fig. The air here was cool and green and all was exceptionally quiet. The creamy fruit seemed to give her strength and she walked for an hour praying that God would guide her footsteps to the forest margin. Why had she been such a fool as to leave the Land Rover? Why? She trudged despondently on with only the deep silence of the living forest and now and again the bell-toned call of a bird.

Though she had seen many snakes, she came to a breathless halt when an amethyst python slithered out of its tight coils to glide up a tree, a dull sheen on its velvety-textured skin. The python was the largest in the tropical rain forest and its great size thrilled and dismayed her. Stealthily she moved away to the left, not daring to pass under the python's tree. It seemed to her glazed eyes that there were coloured lights in the distance, jagged spotlights of sunshine. She brooded over it, thinking it could be a mirage or a figment of her fevered imagination. Still she walked towards it and as she got nearer she could see great banks of flowering lantana alive with butterflies.

They were flying around or resting near this their most common plant food, a dazzling display of brilliant iridescent colour. Now she knew she was on the forest margin, for the lantana dominated the areas around the rain forests and the pink lantana flowers attracted all the butterflies for miles around. How Jeff would love to see this fantastic kaleidoscope of living colour!

She limped closer, fascinated and unbearably elated as though human help was in sight. There were large butterflies with a wing span of perhaps five inches, their beating wings flashing electric blue, then black; spectacular red butterflies, pink butterflies, lime green and yellow, soft brown and white; a tremendous variety of patterns. They fluttered and darted among the prickly flowering masses, not in the least concerned with her presence or the possible attack from insect hunting birds.

If she just kept going she would break out into the open savannah. The thought gave her heart and she made a great effort to pull herself together body and mind. She had been walking, walking, walking.... Please God, someone would find her.

*

He listened with his ears strained. It came again, a faint moan. Again he shouted, calling the name the girl's brother had told him.

'Susan?'

Except for the harsh laughter of a kingfisher there was nothing. He stared fixedly in the direction of that soft moaning sound. There was only silence. He shouted the name again, slashing through the looping rope like vines. A search party had been called out the moment the young man had staggered into base camp. His men had found the abandoned vehicle but no sign of the girl. Little fool! It was certain she had wandered off.

When the news had reached the homestead he had called in trackers, good men, but still she hadn't been found. High up above the forest the sun was a blazing copper disc about to set, the tropic sky a glory of pink and crimson and gold with streaks of vermilion. It was always like this on the verge of the Wet. He had brought the jeep in as far as he could, but he would have to go the rest of the way on foot. Whether night closed in on him or not, he would have to investigate that sound. It was young and dismal and, he would have staked his life on it, human. The girl had been out three days and he well knew what that meant.

The sun was still scorching out in the open, but under the dense canopy of green that rose like some great tent on the border of his property it was cool and almost deathly quiet. He hacked and slashed his way through the undergrowth, instinct telling him he was on the right track. Everything depended on finding her now, and he swung his machete determinedly, stopping now and then to check whether that sound was being repeated.

'God!' he cried aloud, but it wasn't a cry for help. He was filled with a mingled anger and pity for the girl's plight. He had just been about to fly to the State capital when he got the news that two youngsters had been reported missing in the vicinity of Lara. Later the boy had been found and brought in to the homestead sick with anxiety about his sister. How had they ever been allowed to get themselves into such a predicament? Even experienced stockmen lost themselves in the wilds.

Driven by the force of his anger and the desperate need to find the girl, he hacked away at the jungle vegetation that whipped back at him, causing blood to flow. He was a big man, copper-skinned, very dark. His hard, handsome face was completely devoid of emotion. What tensions, what violence he felt he kept under a tight rein. He was about thirty-three or four, no more, though the stamp of authority added a formidable dimension to a striking, somewhat ruthless appearance. He looked, and was, a man who knew power, though he thought considerably less of it than many another rich man.

It was becoming gloomy now that the sun was fast setting and he forged ahead, his eye attracted by a patch of pale colour. Through the branches he caught sight of the girl's body, the face cleanly cut in ivory, the dark red hair bound by leaves like a crown.

The sweat broke out on his hard body and he slashed forward so quickly he trod on a snake's tail, then as it tried to round on him, he neatly severed its head from its body. She looked waxen, yet curiously relaxed like a child, lying in a small clearing in front of a tremendous rain forest tree whose trunk and main branches were covered in a phenomenon called cauliflory, a flowering characteristic found only in rain forest trees. That tree he knew well. He had carved his initials on it as a boy, somewhere beneath those bizarre bunches of white flowers. It struck him very strangely that he should find her there.

At his touch, Susan opened her eyes dazedly, thinking herself still in her dream. A man was bent over her like some grim god, his dark skin golden, the eyes she first thought black, dark green like the forest. There was moisture on her mouth and as she touched her tongue to it she could taste the cool beads of water.

'I was quite sure no one would find me.'

'Don't talk!' he said as though he was angry. With his strong hands at her back he half lifted her, holding his water canteen to her mouth. 'Try a little more. Just a little at a time.'

Her large blue violet eyes looked at him in complexity. 'I believe I was dreaming about you.'

'Drink now,' he said firmly, as though it was perfectly normal to hallucinate.

She did as she was told, a pulse pounding in her neck and throat. The water was so delicious, so wonderfully refreshing, she grabbed at the canteen and drank thirstily, runnels of water trickling down her arched neck and into the open vee of her shirt.

'That's enough!' he said decisively, withdrawing his hand from the back of her head. 'You can have all you want later. Right now I'm concerned with getting you back to the jeep. The light has almost gone.'

She looked around her with a returning sense of

panic, remembering how frightened she had been of the dark. 'I don't think I can walk,' she offered quietly, not absolutely sure everything was real. 'My body doesn't seem to be part of me.'

'Righto then, I'll carry you.' He slipped his arms under her, lifting her as if she was no more than a frail child whose instinct for survival had almost been crushed. 'Keep your head down,' he warned her. 'The fronds of the palms could cut you and the stinging tree grows right along the edge of the forest.'

She hardly heard what he said, her face pressed against his hard chest. From the high, easy way he was carrying her she might have been a bundle of feathers he could carry for miles. Darkness was falling so rapidly he was almost running with her, treading his way expertly through the high tangled vegetation with the eerie miaow of the cat bird the last of the daytime bird sounds. Within moments the forest would be drowned in night and it would be impossible to move.

A sound in the undergrowth triggered the man's quick instincts. He came to an abrupt halt in the oppressive quiet, lowering the girl to the ground so swiftly that in her weakened condition she staggered and fell panting to her knees.

'What is it?' she asked.

'*Quiet!*'

At the sound, that came again, he stepped noiselessly in front of her, his hand on his hunting knife, while Susan slumped to the ground, feeling a wave of nausea. A moment later a huge wild boar broke heavily out of the maze of creepers and cable vines, an ugly indistinct bulk, its little yellow eyes glaring, big curved tusks protruding from clay-daubed jaws.

'No!' In the heat Susan started shivering, such a drumming setting up behind her temples she thought she was going to faint.

'Keep perfectly still!' The man moved back fractionally towards her, his voice absolutely toneless, but without warning Susan wailed and the boar roared and rooted with its feet, then rushed her.

In the instant it rushed past him, the man jerked his powerful arms downwards and sideways, sending the blade of his knife deep into the boar's massive neck. It went down immediately, screaming obscenely, blood spurting in a torrent, colouring the whole of Susan's world.

She reacted in a frenzy, gathering the dregs of her feeble energy, running blindly in an effort to shelter her eyes, but the vines were tugging at her, holding her prisoner, and the man reached her quickly, pulling her shuddering, outraged body back against his hard strength.

'Get a grip on yourself, girl!'

The curt lash of his voice didn't even penetrate her mounting hysteria. She didn't even know she was giving herself up to it, all she knew was that everything was threatening her. Loud whimpering noises were coming up from her throat, pitiful to hear, and he spun her around to him, while she tried to twist away from him, catching a handful of her hair and slapping her face.

'Don't go to pieces now!' he cried deliberately, his eyes brilliant, nostrils flaring, adding to the impression of curbed violence.

'*Oh!*' Her head, that had snapped back, lolled like a flower on a stalk, her mouth opening and closing, no sounds emerging except one crushed little exclamation.

Her hair was cascading about her small face, her cheek showing the imprint of his hand. 'Poor little devil!' There was a softening break in the dark, authoritative voice. 'Slapping children isn't my department, really, but I had to, of course.'

She couldn't move, couldn't speak for several more moments, her heartbeats still wild, while he stood over her, holding her firmly in case she crashed to her knees.

'I don't know how that happened.' It was a pitiful little apology and she winced for the strength in his hands was overpowering. 'I'm sorry.'

'Don't be.' Abruptly he released her. 'Most women would have been half out of their minds.' He moved sideways away from her to slash at some hanging vines. 'I'm afraid we're doomed to spending the night here. The light has almost gone.'

She swallowed and edged closer to him. 'I don't mind so badly now I'm not alone.'

'All right then.' He gave her an impersonal glance. 'I've some food and water and I'll get a fire going right away. It'll keep the mosquitoes away and a whole lot else. It isn't what I hoped to achieve for you, but at least you're safe.'

As he spoke he was gathering fallen wood for the fire, but Susan just stood there watching him, hugging her arms to her slight body, a touching trust in her delicate pale face. 'What would have happened to me if you hadn't been there?' she asked huskily, unable to look back towards the spot where he had killed the boar.

'I *was* there. Let's leave it at that.' He was on his knees setting a match to the dry tinder. 'You got off lightly considering the risks. I'm Devin Chandler,' he flicked her a look. 'We're on the border of my property, Lara. Your brother was brought in safely late yesterday afternoon.'

'Thank God!' Susan said in a soft little gasp. 'I thought of him a zillion times, yet I hadn't even asked.'

'Has there been time?' He looked up at her half ironically. 'How your brother ever acted so foolishly I'll never know. Neither of you have the slightest jungle technique, yet you chose to explore it.'

'Jeff told me to stay put.' She advanced towards the welcoming flame, her face so gentle, so full of love he was half way persuaded she was as sweet and innocent as she looked.

'Maybe next time you'll listen!' A kind of contemptuous mockery was in his frosted eyes, though she could have knelt at his feet in gratitude. 'Come, sit down!' His voice softened almost involuntarily. 'The night will pass quickly and I'll have you out of here at first light.'

'I want to tell you how grateful I am.'

'You don't have to!' He gave a tight smile. 'I understand, blue eyes.'

She was so lightheaded he put up his hand to help her to the ground. 'What you need is food!' he said crisply. 'What have you been surviving on?'

'Oh, this and that,' she answered vaguely. 'I had a packet of biscuits and a bar of chocolate and I've been eating berries and bananas. The water ran out this morning—I was rationing it out of the canteen. I didn't know how dreadful it is to be thirsty. Far, far worse than going hungry.'

'There's water, but you didn't know where to find it.' He turned away from her to rummage in his pack.

She could hear his voice, but it was fading and she clutched at his arm. 'I feel giddy. I think I'm going to faint.'

Immediately he had his arm around her, holding her head down. 'Help yourself by breathing in and out quietly. It's not necessary for you to move or speak until the feeling has passed.'

'I ... I....'

'Go easy,' he said, his fingers massaging her nape. She seemed to have slipped sideways, half lying against him with her eyes closed, her breasts against the hardness of his body, her delicate oval face beneath his so pale it accentuated the dark ruby glow of her hair and the heavy fringe of lashes.

'I can see I'll have to feed you,' he said quietly. 'You'll feel stronger when you've had something to eat.'

She nodded her head, all softness and silky skin, and his eyes raked her, afraid she would pass out. He eased away from her, then back again, putting his hand to her face. 'Think you can manage a sandwich?'

Their eyes connected and she shook her head to clear it. 'I'll be all right now.'

'I hope so!' He put the sandwich firmly into her hand. 'When you're a little bit better, I'll see to the tea.'

'Really?' Her violet blue eyes had a clinging fascination. 'That would be marvellous!'

'Don't expect milk!' The firelight touching his dark face made it look almost satanic. 'Keep going on that sandwich.'

'I will!' She bit into it and looked at him. 'I don't feel so peculiar now.'

'Mmm.' He got to his lean powerful height, looking as though he didn't believe her. 'You can't help it.'

'You don't despise me, do you?' she asked him on impulse, mystified by some expression in his eyes.

'Don't talk, *eat*!' he returned bluntly.

'Okay,' she said softly, as though desperate to please him. 'I know I've put you to a lot of bother.'

'Not just you. Your brother.' He looked at her, saw her face, then smiled, and it reached her like an actual electric shock. A man who could smile like that could wound a woman deeply, break down her every defence. Up until now he had personified Man, the Protector, but now she was able to see he was infinitely, dangerously, attractive, able to inflict pain. The thought and many others, kept her silent until after he had made the tea and they had both had a drink. Her throat wasn't dry now and she could feel a little of her strength returning.

'In another minute you'll have got yourself all together,' he observed, when she finally dared look at him.

'That was the best meal of my life!' she said with endearing gratitude.

'I suppose it was at that!' he gave a faint laugh. 'How old are you anyway?'

'Twenty-two.' All around them were the black and twisting trees and she drew nearer to him for comfort.

'You look younger.' His green gaze sharpened over her.

'That's because I feel so helpless.'

'Dependent, you mean?'

'Yes.' She shook her head dumbly, aware that he regarded women, even the best of them, as a damned nuisance.

'What made you decide to leave your vehicle?' he asked in the same terse tone.

'Don't laugh at me, but I was afraid the ferns and the vines would just grow over me and no one would find me again.'

'Good God!' There was supreme confidence in the very set of his dark head and his lean, powerful body. 'You're supposed to sit tight in that kind of situation. My men found the Land Rover first thing this morning.'

'So I broke an important rule.'

'Probably it's easy for a slip of a girl, but....'

'Don't blame Jeff!' she interrupted determinedly. 'We've come thousands of miles without mishap and he's taken very good care of me.'

He waved that away impatiently 'So you live with your brother?'

'No. We just decided to take a holiday together. It was the wonderful adventure we'd looked forward to all our lives.'

'I take it you haven't any fiancé or anything?'

'I haven't even thought about it,' she protested, one hand coming up to touch her warm cheek.

'I bet you're the only one who hasn't!' he returned sardonically. 'Do you think you could sleep now?'

'I want to, so badly!' She looked away from him as though she were going to cry. 'It seems a miracle you found me. The nights were the hardest to bear—no light from anywhere and the forest alive with all kinds of furry things. I think I was more frightened of the sugar gliders and the tree rats than the bats and the snakes.'

'Put it out of your mind,' he said firmly. 'You've been lucky.'

Susan looked at him and was swept by unfamiliar complex sensations. 'I wouldn't have lasted another day,' she said, and her mouth trembled.

'It would be more sensible to make your mind a blank so you could sleep!' The crispness of his tone halted her.

'All right!' Rather timidly she touched his arm. 'I'll find some way to thank you properly.'

'That's not necessary.'

'You sound angry?' Distress sounded in her voice.

'Not at all!' He rose abruptly and moved away from her. 'I just don't want you to get bogged down emotionally. You've been through an ordeal.'

'Yet it was really so beautiful.' She stared up at his tall, wide-shouldered figure as though it had great drawing power.

'The rain forest?' He turned his green glance on her.

'What else?'

'You're a strange child.' His mouth relaxed a fraction.

'Because I find the rain forest beautiful?' For a moment spirit made her eyes flash. 'I know it was stupid and dangerous to go exploring without a guide, but it's been amazing. We came from the Centre to all this. It's overwhelming, the luxuriance.'

'To some it's alien and hostile.'

'Not to me, now I'm not alone.' Her eyelids were drooping of their own accord and he came back towards her, his hand closing over her shoulder gently, compelling her to the ground and the softness of the moss he had gathered.

'You won't go away?' she managed anxiously.

'I'll be right here.' His eyes brooded on her uncertain face. 'Sleep easily, little one. In the morning I'll take you back to the homestead.'

'Lara,' she said dreamily. 'I've heard of it. A private kingdom where a man makes his own laws.'

'No place for a flower child like you.' He pushed something cushiony beneath her head, watching her heavy eyelashes flickering.

With a tremendous effort she opened her eyes, staring back at him. 'It's a lovely feeling to know I'm safe. Thank you.'

'Lie still. You're almost asleep.' Strands of her dark red hair clung to her cheek and almost involuntarily he brushed them away. 'No, I don't want to hear another sound out of you,' he commanded, as her eyes clung to him and her mouth trembled to say a little more. 'Goodnight.'

All her strength had gone now, but she wasn't frightened any more. The nightmare was over and Jeff was safe. She sank into her soft bed of moss with peace and the scented aroma of sandalwood surrounding her.

In the early hours of the morning she awoke with the sound of her own terrified cries echoing in her exhausted, overwrought mind. Iron arms were holding her and drawing her close to a hard, male body. She started to scream then, her eyes filling with tears and her breast heaving, pushing with all her might against this powerful aggressor, a dark shape in the night.

'Susan, stop it! You're dreaming ... *dreaming*.'

The voice, she knew it. She fell back against the confining arms, her voice hoarse in her throat, immediately aware of her surroundings as full consciousness returned.

'I'm sorry!' Her voice trembled and she burst out crying.

'It's all right,' he said quietly. 'Cry out if you want to.'

'*No!*' Her hands were balling into small fists and she tried to sit upright. 'What a fool you must think me.'

'You're brave enough,' he answered abruptly.

'It was the boar,' she whispered unsteadily. 'It was coming straight for me again.'

They were so close he could feel her frantic fear right through her body. 'Do you think you could go back to sleep if you stayed right where you are?'

'But I can't let you ... you'd be taking my weight,' she protested weakly.

'You're no burden.' Already his strong confident hands were settling her protectively within the circle of his arms. 'Besides, it's human contact you need.'

He was looking down at her so commandingly, there was nothing else to do but subside against him. The terror of her dream was receding, but her heart was still beating fast. Everything that had happened, being lost, then rescued in this beautiful pitiless wilderness, was strange to her, but nothing more strange than being cradled in this imperious man's arms.

She sighed deeply and brushed the tears from her face. Her head fell back against his shoulder and her melancholy, deep blue eyes closed. He was strong, the strongest man she had ever known, and she owed him her life.

CHAPTER TWO

By late afternoon of the same day, Susan was looking and feeling much better. She sat propped up against the pillows in a large, beautifully furnished bedroom in Lara homestead, looking towards the panelled bedroom door. Someone was turning the brass knob and in the next instant the door opened, then shut softly behind her brother.

'So you're awake!' Jeff's good-looking face was filled with heartfelt relief.

'Hi!' Susan smiled at him reassuringly and waved her slender expressive hands. 'I'm not used to being treated like Royalty.'

'Be sure I'm not getting the same treatment,' her brother returned ruefully. He pulled up a chair to the bedside and took hold of his sister's hand, patting the fingers that curled around his so affectionately. 'You're looking so much better now,' he told her earnestly. 'It was worth the ticking off from Chandler to see you so safe and cosseted. He made me feel a total fool, and I deserved it.'

'Then he wasn't being fair to you!' Susan's blue-violet eyes glowed. 'I should have stayed with the Land Rover just like you told me. He wasn't too hard on you, was he?'

Jeff shook his head despairingly. 'We can only hope not to bother him again. Anyway, he was right. I had no business exposing you to danger. I've never seen you looking so fragile and big-eyed as when he brought you in. You mean more to me than anyone else in the world.'

'That will change!' Susan smiled slightly. 'Anyway, we should be able to get away tomorrow. The doctor said all I needed was a good rest.'

'You don't believe Chandler will let you?' Jeff almost screeched. 'Believe me, kiddo, you'll do nothing without *his* say-so. I've been long enough on Lara to know his word is law, so don't go making any hasty decisions. Besides, you're not strong enough to go anywhere.'

Susan's face framed in her lustrous red hair was pale and faintly pinched, hollows under her cleanly modelled cheekbones. 'Darling, you sound so strained.'

'I know that.' Jeff looked away from her. 'It's Chandler, his assessment of me. I'd never do anything to hurt you, you know that.'

'Of course!' Susan looked anxiously at her brother's taut, good-looking face. 'I'm sorry he gave you such a bad time, but I can be ready to leave in the morning. We'll go across to the Reef and laze in the sun. No experience is useless, Jeff, and the important thing is we've survived.'

'Thanks to Chandler. I've never felt so horribly futile and helpless in my life these past few days. A man like Chandler learnt early how to govern himself, and everyone else so far as I can see.'

'Someone has to be lucky,' Susan answered a little flatly. 'He's a big, commanding man and he doesn't suffer fools gladly, but he saved my life and in his way he was very kind. I'd never have held up without him.'

'I know, a real hero!' Jeff laughed a little painfully. 'It's demoralising to be made to feel an irresponsible idiot. *That* experience I'll never forget.'

Susan understood her brother was feeling sorry for himself and she was swift to answer him. 'Probably as community leader he takes his duty seriously, but we're not part of his tribe. Tomorrow we're leaving.'

'No, love,' Jeff gave a faint grimace. 'Give yourself time. If you got up now you'd be just dragging yourself round. Let Chandler decide, he's the big man.'

'Maybe I don't intend to pay as much mind to him as everyone else!'

'Next suggestion?' Jeff laughed, looking eased, and pushed his sister back gently into the pillows. 'Reaction will probably hit you tomorrow. Lie quiet and get better.'

'I *am* better!' Susan insisted, feeling quite clear-headed and in control of herself. 'We made a mistake, but we can live with it and it didn't end in tragedy. I'll rest tonight and tomorrow I'll speak up. I'm sure Mr Chandler doesn't want to get stuck with us.'

'Once you see around the place you won't want to leave it!' Jeff was suddenly enthusiastic and distracted. 'This is a different world, so big and free. No wonder a man gets to be so proud and confident. What a challenge to establish possession of a big holding like this, a lush, tropical paradise. I've been talking to the men and riding the horses. Lara is one of the finest cattle stations in the State and the Chandler family pioneered the North. Apparently they even owned a goldmine at one time. The natives call him Byamee, Man of Great Strength. He's the symbol of authority around here, so breach an order at your peril.'

From being mortified, Jeff was now amused, happy to talk on and on about this legendary station and a family who had risked their lives to establish order then prosperity on the virgin wilderness. 'I'd really like to work here for a time.'

'You'd *what?*' Susan sat forward urgently.

'Oh, it's impossible, I know.' Jeff glanced back at her startled face. 'I never really thought about it until just now and it just popped out. It's all so interesting, and we're so near the ocean. Apparently Chandler has a beautiful yacht and he's cruised all round the islands. He even designed it, I believe, and obviously he's not short of money. It must be some craft.'

'But we can't stay——' Susan touched his hand tentatively, aware of her brother's burning enthusiasms. 'Even if Mr Chandler took you on as a hand, he'd work you until you dropped.'

'It would still be a dream!' Jeff maintained, his blue eyes on fire. 'Man, you're liberated up here—and have you ever seen such sunsets? It's so beautiful I don't think I could ever live in a city again.'

'What about me?' Susan asked quietly. 'Or are you proposing to find me a job in the cookhouse?'

'Don't be silly!' Jeff said softly. 'In any case, you're not equipped to do the cooking. They need someone strong and not pretty enough to start the men fighting. To tell the truth, Chandler doesn't employ females.'

'And the answer for that is plain enough,' Susan returned a little tartly. 'I don't think he admires them.'

'He just *has* to admire his sister-in-law,' Jeff commented with a gleam in his eyes.

'I thought that was Mrs Chandler.' Susan recalled a tall, slim blonde vision who had hovered in the background when she was brought in.

'So it is!' Jeff answered, whistling under his breath.

'Would you like me to tell you more?'

'Not if it's gossip,' Susan sighed, a little bewildered by the relief she felt at Jeff's news. What did it matter to her if Devin Chandler had a beautiful blonde wife?

Jeff's blue eyes were glinting and he seemed to be looking piercingly into her face. 'Apparently the younger brother, Brad, was killed in a plane crash about two years ago, a charter flight that came down in an electrical storm killing the pilot and his three passengers, all prominent business men.'

'How awful!' said Susan, her profile to her brother.

'But really, they're terribly dangerous, aren't they, light aircraft?' Jeff commented, knowing very little about them. 'Anyway, Felicia, that's her name, had some kind of a breakdown and came here to recuperate. She's been here for six weeks or more. No one actually said anything, but I got the impression she was once involved with Big Brother but married brother Brad instead. There's a kiddy, a plain little thing about seven or eight. How she got that way I can't imagine, with such a beautiful mother.'

'Children change,' Susan advised him. 'Take my advice and don't discuss Mrs Chandler with anyone.'

'But it's the other way round!' Jeff defended himself. 'Everyone up here takes a great interest in everyone else and despite the fair Felicia's beauty none of the staff seem to like her.'

'A nice commentary,' Susan said wryly.

'She seems to have a patrician contempt for them, or maybe that's just her beautiful cold face. I've only spoken to her twice and she didn't even answer me, just inclined her ash-blonde head. Do you think it's real? I don't think I've ever seen hair that colour before.'

'I'll decide when I meet her,' said Susan, and lay back. 'You're not staying at the house?'

'No, I'm with Harry Tindall and his wife. Harry's Chandler's overseer, a great bloke, and they have plenty of room for me in their bungalow, especially since their girl got married. I think Mary likes having me there. She's a very sweet, motherly woman, Pamela's direct opposite.'

'Did any of this get into the papers?' Susan cut in swiftly, thinking she was a fool not to have thought of it before. She was wearing an exquisite ice-blue night-gown that certainly didn't belong to her and the lace fluttered over her agitated breast.

'Calm down, calm down.' Jeff leaned forward to clasp her hand. 'Chandler got word to Dad. It got into the papers all right, but by the time they mentioned names, you'd been found. I ought to tell you Chandler's discovered all there is to know about us, but at least he went right out of his way to put Dad's mind at ease. You know, he's only eight years older than I am, yet he seems much, much older, as though he came into the world complete and powerful. I know he made me very angry with myself. I was certain I'd never see you again, your small face framed in curls and your eyes glowing. You're a very beautiful girl, Susie, I can't help remarking.' He bent down and kissed her cheek, then stood up from the bed. 'I probably won't see you any more today. I had to beg Chandler's permission just to pop in on you now. Take care.'

'You too.' Susan smiled at him radiantly, all her love for him in her face. 'Perhaps I'll be allowed to get up in the morning.'

'The Boss will tell you that!' Jeff answered, somewhat dryly. 'Harry's going to let me ride out with him in the morning. We'll be bringing some cleanskins in and checking on the herd. There was a big lift of cattle some months ago. Not on this property, it's pretty well patrolled, but further south. I thought the days of cattle duffing were over, but it still goes on, I hear. The beef roads make it fairly easy to move a lot of cattle fast.'

'There's no danger, is there?' Susan's pale face was faintly flushed.

'There's always danger, kiddo!' Jeff said with a swagger. 'I don't mind for myself. It's just you I never want to see hurt. Harry knows all the old stories. Some of them would curl your hair if it wasn't so curly already. This was called the Wild North. It still is, as we found out.'

'It fascinates you, I can see that!' Susan glanced at her brother's slim, compact figure, feeling the exhilaration in him.

'Can you blame me if I want to see more?'

She shook her head, remembering how he had been all his life, his thirst for adventure. 'Just be careful and don't try riding hell-for-leather. It's not the same as hacking around at home.'

'Harry says I'm a natural.'

'You're that!' she answered gaily. 'Do you think anyone will give me something to eat?'

Jeff, already at the door, turned to walk back to her. 'Shall I ask? There's a housekeeper and plenty of household staff.'

'No, don't bother.' The delicate rose tint in Susan's cheeks and lips had deepened. 'I'm being so well looked after I'm sure someone will come. What time is it anyway?'

'Just after five.' Jeff glanced at the watch on his wrist. 'Probably the Great Man will look in on you himself.'

'I hope not!' Susan's heart unaccountably began to beat rapidly. 'This nightgown's too big for me.'

'It's very fetching all the same.' Jeff smiled at her quick flush. 'Just relax against the cushions and look like a sweet little kitten. What you've been through is enough to put anyone to bed for a week.'

There was a sound of tapping behind him and Jeff turned and went to the door opening it. 'Oh, it's you, Mr Chandler!' It came out very deferential, in spite of himself.

Devin Chandler glanced at the young man without seeming interest, then walked past him into the room.

'You slept?' he asked Susan.

'Yes.' Like Jeff, she too sounded very young and respectful, gazing up at him shyly with her hands folded quietly outside the pale lemon sheet.

'I'll see you tomorrow then, Susan!' Jeff spoke directly to his sister and prepared to depart.

'I should think I'll be ready to leave by then,' Susan said quickly in a now-or-never kind of tone.

'Far too ambitious!' Devin Chandler answered her quite unemotionally. 'It will be all of a week before you're ready to set off again on your travels.'

'Thank you, sir,' Jeff said quietly. 'I'll say goodnight.'

'Goodnight!' Chandler answered, briefly turning his dark head. 'When you go out tomorrow with Harry, do exactly as you're told. I understand your desire to try everything at once, but I don't want to hear about any severe falls or any other injuries. It's easy enough to come down in a tangle when you're chasing calves. Just don't let them dive under your horse's neck.'

'I won't!' Jeff's expression said he expected it would be great fun. ' 'Night, Sis!'

'Take care!' she said to him, as one invariably did to brothers with a reckless streak.

'He seems very keen to become a stockman,' Devin Chandler remarked as Jeff's footsteps sounded down the passageway.

'He's been keen to be a lot of things!' Susan tried to reply lightly, but the dark green eyes were touching her face, her skin, and her voice had gone husky.

'You're looking much better,' he told her.

'Truly, I *am*. I'd like to get up tomorrow.'

'It wouldn't hurt you to wander around the house,' he said as though he were being sympathetic to a child's request. 'I hope you're feeling hungry?'

Inexplicably she wasn't. Not since he had come into the room, filling it with all kinds of male radiations. He wore a gauze weight linen shirt with an easy, open neck in olive green that went well with a snakeskin belt and classic tan slacks and he looked very relaxed and stylish and very self-assured. Nothing at all like the man one would expect to meet in the wilds, except that his body was hard, in superb condition, and his European skin was burnt to a smooth, polished teak.

'Well?' he repeated. 'You must be satisfied I'm the same man who brought you out of the jungle.'

'I don't like to disrupt your household.' He must have thought her crazy, the way she was staring at him.

'What does one do, throw you out?' He gave her a mocking smile. 'Everyone in the district knows you've had a rough time of it. Just try to relax. By the end of the week you should have gained a few pounds and then I'll feel happier about letting you go.'

'Can't I get up and have dinner?' Her beautiful blue eyes pleaded with him.

'You really are coming along!' His smile sent a flood of colour into her face. 'All right, but what are you going to wear?'

'Well ...' she glanced down at the expensive filmy nightgown, 'what happened to my things?'

'Jess will tell you.' He was brisk all of a sudden. 'Jess is my housekeeper. You met her before.'

'Of course!' Susan lifted her head to look at him. 'She was very kind to me.'

'She should be!' The brilliant, lancing eyes flicked across her face. 'She's also sent me along to make sure you're going to eat a good dinner.'

'I'll surprise you,' she promised, feeling oddly elated.

'Good—we'd better see about getting you something to wear.'

Some little time later Susan met Felicia Chandler at last. She was a striking-looking ash-blonde with unexpectedly dark eyes, her tall, slim body as elegantly clothed as a *Vogue* model. Though it was easy to see she would dazzle many men, she didn't make the slightest attempt to put nameless nobodies at their ease, especially when they were twenty-two-year-old girls like Susan.

'Where do you come from?' she asked, looking Susan straight up and down.

'Melbourne.' Susan was feeling distinctly uncomfortable, unwilling to try on the few garments Felicia

had draped over one of a pair of deep armchairs upholstered in a Chinoiserie chintz.

'You know you put an end to an important trip of
Dev's?'

'No, I didn't.'

'Well, you did. Most definitely.' Felicia turned to
her and gave a tight little smile. 'There's not very much
of you, is there?'

'I'm not usually as frail-looking as this.' Susan looked
down at herself. Of course a part of it was Felicia's long
nightgown, but she had lost close to seven pounds.
'Thank you for the loan of your nightgown. I should
have realised it was yours.'

'Keep it!' said Felicia, not at all kindly. 'Really, my
dear, I don't seem to have brought anything that might
fit you. You're so short.'

'Five feet three isn't all that tiny,' Susan answered,
feeling hot and uncomfortable. 'It's kind of you to
bother, but we're not at all of a size.'

'Well, at least we've given you sanctuary!' Felicia
gave the same tight smile that scarcely moved her
mouth and never touched her eyes. 'Why don't you
have a quiet dinner in your room and your own things
should be here by the morning. Dev sent a man for
them—also to fix up your motel bill.'

'But that wasn't necessary. We could have done that
when we got back. The proprietor would know the
story.'

'It's nothing!' Felicia waved her hand, her scent in
the warm room almost mesmerising. 'Everyone leans on
Dev, always have, always will.'

'I didn't set out to lose myself,' Susan pointed out
quietly.

'I understand that, dear,' Felicia was very short about it, 'but you're pretty helpless right at the minute.'

'Just a bit weak, otherwise fine. I'm sure in another day my brother and I will be away from here.'

'Don't get emotional about it!' Felicia lifted her hand to the nape of her neck, checking her cool, upswept hairdo was staying that way. She was made up quite a bit, her dark eyes outlined in black, and though she was fair-skinned, Susan judged correctly that her hair had once been as dark as her arching brows. 'Are you sure there isn't anything else I could do for you before I go?' she asked coolly, scrutinising her immaculate image in the full-length mirror.

'No, thank you.' Susan tried to keep the stiffness out of her voice.

'Keep the robe at least.' Felicia gestured vaguely towards a sensational blue silk creation. 'Of course it will trail all over the floor, but it won't matter on the carpet. If you're really interested I'll show you over the house before you go. It's seen a lot of dramas and it has great atmosphere. I never feel better than when I come home to Lara, and Dev's the one man I know I can always rely on.'

She didn't linger any longer but picked up the two dresses she should never have selected in the first place. 'I'll tell Mrs Hansen you'll be having dinner in your room, but it's much the better way, wouldn't you say?'

Susan didn't have to answer, for as Felicia reached the door and opened it Jess Hansen stepped brightly across the threshold with a pile of clothing over her arm. 'Well, my dear, you're looking really splendid now!' Snapping blue eyes in a broad homely face and a look of dependability marked Devin Chandler's housekeeper.

'What have you got there, Mrs Hansen?' Felicia asked abruptly, as though the housekeeper had no right to be there at all.

'One or two things.' Mrs Hansen glanced calmly away from Felicia's strangely set face. 'I just knew your lovely things wouldn't suit, this young lady being so much smaller. I just popped over to Mary Tindall's and borrowed some of Jill's things. I don't know why I didn't think of it before. She got herself a whole new wardrobe before she got married, so there was plenty she left behind for when she comes to stay. Mary pulled these things out for the moment. She certainly wants to meet you, dear, when you're well enough to walk over to the bungalow. Your brother's already made himself something of a favourite.'

'That was really very nice of you, Mrs Hansen.' Susan took the pile of clothing that was handed to her, 'And Mrs Tindall. I'll go across tomorrow and thank her. Jeff told me how kind she's been to him.'

'Nothing very inspired there, I'm afraid,' Felicia drawled, 'but it was sweet of both ladies to think of you.'

When she was alone again Susan ran the bath in the adjoining bathroom, took off the nightgown and climbed in the scented tub. Both the bedroom and the bathroom were decorated to a woman's taste, not only beautiful but comfortable, and she had ventured to use the big bottle of pink bath salts that stood on the edge of the handsomely tile-enclosed tub.

What difference did it make if Felicia Chandler disliked her on sight? Or was she the same with everyone?

Certainly hers wasn't a warm, outgoing personality and Mrs Hansen had thrown her a conspiratorial wink. Susan laughed openly at the memory, catching sight of herself in the mirrored wall. She had caught her hair on top of her head with a clasp she had found in the top drawer of the bureau, but soft tendrils escaped from the thick, lustrous coil, damp, glinting red against the creamy pallor of cheek and temple and nape. At odd times, such as now, she became aware of her own beauty, her satiny woman's body. The tips of her breasts were visible above the pink bubbles, her skin gleaming, superb skin, all of it. She had inherited that from her mother, plus her sometimes violet eyes and the dark red of her hair.

Last night she had slept with a kittenlike sinuousness in the arms of a stranger. The mirrored wall was misting over and she was glad of it. There was something in her face she hadn't seen before, a sensuousness—the eyes a little panic-stricken, the soft, full-lipped mouth almost hungry for a man's kisses. She couldn't believe it and it made her feel frightened. Tremulously she stood up in the bath and dried herself quickly with a thick, fluffy towel, feeling the fragrance from the bath salts emanating from her, breathing in its scent. In some ways she was a very young twenty-two and no man had ever complicated her life. Devin Chandler. Just stop thinking about him. Just stop!

Over dinner Susan saw Felicia Chandler in a different light. For a woman who had reportedly suffered a breakdown she talked and laughed effortlessly, smiling in what Susan considered a disconcerting fashion into her brother-in-law's eyes.

'Be a dear, darling, do please open another bottle of champagne. It's all I drink!'

Devin Chandler gave a dry laugh and got to his feet. 'In that case I'll keep where I stash it a secret.'

'Not you, darling, I've often thought you're much too generous!' Lingeringly she laid her hand on his arm, her almost white hair and her fluid yellow dress absorbing all the light.

'What about you, Susan?' Chandler's eyes stared in Susan's direction.

'Thank you, no. I only allow myself a glass.'

'How so?' Felicia asked, mock pleasantly.

'I'm not used to it, so I'd better not trifle with it,' Susan answered lightly.

'What nonsense!' Felicia drawled. 'It will do you good.'

Behind them Mrs Hansen and a little aboriginal housegirl deftly removed the dishes and Felicia fell silent as though with her brother-in-law gone she found Susan very difficult to talk to. Jess Hansen at the great mahogany sideboard beamed at Susan with approval, thinking she had never seen Jill's little floral cotton voile dress look so good. It was gaily printed with flowers on a deep ultramarine ground and the girl's colouring and dancer's body even allowed it to compete with Felicia's silky cotton jersey with a predictable exclusive label.

'That was a beautiful meal, Mrs Hansen,' Susan smiled, speaking directly to the housekeeper.

'I'm glad you enjoyed it, dear!' Mrs Hansen smiled back at her naturally, but became aware of Felicia's stony profile and withdrew to the kitchen to prepare the coffee.

Felicia looked across at Susan as though driven at last to speak to her. 'I don't think you told me what you do when you're not getting yourself lost?'

'I'm a schoolteacher.' Susan coloured faintly.

'A schoolteacher?' Felicia stared at her. 'What an extraordinary thing to be!'

'I find it very rewarding,' Susan answered, a little startled.

'I mean no criticism, dear!' Felicia seemed to apologise, 'but you're very shy, aren't you, to be a schoolteacher. You must have no effect on the children.'

'I suppose they see me quite differently from you,' Susan managed politely. 'Actually I'm quite good at my job. I enjoy it and I'm very fond of the young.'

'How nice of you to explain,' Felicia smiled. 'You're really quite a good-looking girl, a little gauche maybe, but I expect you'll soon abandon your career for marriage?'

'There's no one in my life at the moment,' Susan said, sitting there with the soft, brilliant light from the overhead chandelier flashing out all the ruby tints in her hair.

'But you're a romantic, aren't you, dear?' Felicia seemed to want to pursue it. 'I mean, you look so *soft!*'

'As in mushy?' Susan replied a little tartly. Gentle and sensitive by nature, she still had the redhead's quick temper.

Felicia laughed a little uncertainly. 'How quick you are to take offence, dear. Tell me a little about yourself —who your parents are, why you decided to go roaming around the countryside with your brother. He seems to be just that wee bit irresponsible.'

'Because we happened to get lost in the jungle?'

Susan challenged her quickly. 'Mrs Hansen told me it was happening all the time. It's very beautiful up here, very lush and wild—unfortunately we knew too little about the dangers. But we've travelled for thousands of miles without mishap. My brother is very dear to me. I'm lucky to have him.'

'Yes, it's heartwarming, such affection,' Felicia observed after a minute. 'Surely your parents couldn't have been happy about letting you go off? Some girls manage to look very confident and capable, but you seem different somehow, as though you've had a very sheltered upbringing.'

'I suppose I have,' Susan answered slowly. 'A very ordinary quiet life. Jeff is different. He always wanted to get away, to see new places, new people. When he planned our trip he made it sound so exciting I wanted to come myself. Life goes by so quickly....'

'Oh, you're very old!' Devin Chandler had come back into the room carrying a bottle of champagne in an ice bucket and he looked down at Susan half mockingly, half teasingly.

'And she wants to fall in love!' Felicia said sweetly, as though Susan had confided in her.

'I didn't say that!' Susan answered in a low voice.

'Frightened?' Devin Chandler asked crisply, rejoining them at the table.

'Perhaps that's only being smart,' Felicia answered for Susan rather bitterly. 'Loving, wanting, can be a shattering experience. Not that this child here is in any great danger. Probably she'll marry some nice dependable young man and live happily ever after.'

'At all costs let's not talk of love and marriage!'

Devin Chandler said suavely, and began to pour his sister-in-law another glass of wine. 'I don't think I told you, Felicia, the Conrads are flying in some time tomorrow afternoon. I've asked them to stay on for a few days.'

'But isn't that a pleasant surprise!' Felicia's somewhat hard voice softened miraculously.

'The Conrads are close friends,' Devin Chandler explained briefly to Susan. 'Bob is one of our most successful business men, with a finger in every pie, he's also one of the best game fishermen in the country. We've had some wonderful times together.'

'World records, Australian records—how these men enjoy themselves!' Felicia proclaimed, flourishing her drink. 'I suppose you know the Great Barrier Reef, Susan?'

'Well, no,' said Susan. 'Jeff and I are hoping to be able to get across to one of the islands.'

'I'll take you while you're here,' Devin Chandler offered completely unexpectedly.

'Darling, you're mad!' Felicia eyed him with perturbation in her dark eyes. 'Susan simply won't be here long enough and now you've got Bob and Trish. Thank heaven Susan will understand.'

'Of course!' Susan turned quickly to her host, only to find him studying her as though he could read her very mind. 'Really, I don't: ...' She was caught by his eyes and left floundering.

'You don't really think I wasted so much time finding you without sending you off knowing the North? The hospitality up here, my child, is very good. Besides, we'll enjoy having you around. You must be, with your job and the way you look, very sympathetic to children.

Felicia's little girl, Emma, my niece, would benefit from your company.'

'Do you really think so?' Felicia asked a little fiercely. 'Poor little pet has just withdrawn from contact since her father died. She won't unbend and she won't talk. I don't think anyone as young and inexperienced as Susan here could help very much. Emma needs professional help. I'm the child's mother, yet she treats me like a stranger.'

'Don't upset yourself, Flick,' Devin Chandler said quietly, then turned his dark head, his eyes on Susan. 'Tomorrow I want you to meet Emma, though we're telling you in advance you might find it difficult to break through her defences. Still, I think you know what hell it is for a child to lose a beloved parent. Emma idolised her father. No one could help loving Brad, my brother. He was a good man. Very good.'

Something Susan couldn't recognise flared in Felicia's dark eyes, some dreadful thought, some rebellion, but she said nothing as she tossed back the last of her drink.

'Susan?' Devin Chandler arched his black brows at her, demanding an answer.

She tried one, though she knew in her bones that she shouldn't accept his invitation. He wasn't safe. She looked at his mouth and away from it. It was beautifully cut, well defined, the mouth of a man with strong passions however strict his self-discipline. He made her feel shyer, more nervous, more a woman, than she ever imagined possible. Don't try and bend me, she thought. Please don't. I'm no match for you.

'Are you really so afraid of accepting my invitation?' His voice was vibrant with mockery, as he settled back in his magnificently carved high-backed chair.

'You've done enough for me already!' She refused to look into those very deep green eyes.

'All right then, you owe me something. Indulge my wish. See everything the tropics have to offer as my guest. All I want in return is for you to enjoy yourself and perhaps in the process help my troubled little niece.'

'I can't bear to see a child unhappy,' Susan said in a low voice.

'Do you think we can?' Felicia was bitterly direct.

'I'm very sorry, Mrs Chandler. I realise that.' Susan winced visibly as Felicia rebuked her. 'Of course, I haven't the training to help your little daughter.'

'If it helps,' Devin Chandler interrupted grimly, 'the professionals couldn't help her either. Emma feels herself very much alone. She's been hurt, badly hurt, and she's retreated into a world of her own. What she needs is some understanding companionship, someone outside the family. Felicia's had no easy time herself and Brad and I were just enough alike for Emma to seem to avoid me. I really wouldn't know.'

'But darling, you know she's relaxed a lot since we've been back on Lara.' Felicia's long-fingered white hand tugged at her brother-in-law's sleeve. 'You mustn't think it's you. You *can't*. Emma used to adore you in the old days. You couldn't have forgotten.'

'She's turning away from real life,' he said, a stormy look on his dark face.

'I know.' Felicia's head drooped pathetically.

'I don't know what I could do,' Susan found herself saying, 'but I could try to talk to her. Maybe she'll tell a stranger, an outsider, what's all bottled up inside her.'

'I don't like your chances, dear!' Felicia's voice was hostile, even frigid, when it seemed to Susan she couldn't possibly object to the idea of one young person extending a little warmth and comfort to another.

'We're not looking for a miracle, Flick,' Devin Chandler pointed out almost brusquely. 'Personally I think it will help to have Susan around, not only because she's young and used to children, but she's not very strong herself. Make no mistake, what she suffered was an ordeal and she's come out of it remarkably well. A few weeks from now, with her head full of pleasant memories, we'll return her to her father and her own world.'

'But what about Jeff?' Susan looked at him as if she knew she was being expertly manipulated.

'Jeff will survive. We might even toughen him up. He's an adventurer, a young man who takes risks, but he can't take risks with his sister's life. Besides, he told me it was the end of your trip. Once you'd seen the Reef he was taking you back home.'

'You appear to have had quite a conversation with him?' Susan didn't know it, but she had tilted her chin, with its shallow dimple.

'Now that you mention it, we did!' A glimmer of amusement came into his eyes. 'Your brother will make out fine. I'm not so sure about you.'

'Give in, Susan, you can't hope to win.' Felicia's eyes conveyed that the whole thing was against her better judgment. 'Dev makes all the decisions around here.'

'I don't know. I must think.' Despite her effort to speak calmly, Susan's mouth trembled. She was conscious of two warring emotions, a strange excitement and a warning constraint, and it showed in her large violet eyes.

'Sleep on it,' Devin Chandler suggested, some nuance in his voice urging her to lift her head.

So what was she supposed to do? she thought as their gaze became locked. He was such a compelling man, yet she had an overwhelming desire to run. But where? Hadn't she told him she would find some way to repay him? It seemed he was just sufficiently ruthless to hold her to her promise. There was a curious expression on his handsome dark face, a flash in his eyes that affected her like a drug. It was odd, but she couldn't catch her breath, couldn't turn her head away ... couldn't escape.

'Let's get off the whole subject,' Felicia said with a great restlessness. 'I certainly don't blame you, Susan, for wanting to go your own way. In fact I think it's much the best idea. We're coming in to the cyclone season and nothing will help my poor little darling, except time!'

In the morning the sun was shining brilliantly, jewel-coloured parrots screeching good morning from the groves of native trees that surrounded the house. Susan blinked her eyes and stretched luxuriously, her fantasies of the night before absurd in the light of day. Devin Chandler had no interest in her at all. She had no worries, no problems there. He was a mature, experienced man of the world, a man moreover of wealth and power. There was no attraction between them. Indeed, it seemed he regarded her in somewhat the same light as his niece, someone to be protected and provided for. This feeling, the fascination, excitement, was all on her side. She had always believed in love, a powerful, over-whelming emotion, and she was long overdue for her first crush. It was no more than that, and they had met so dramatically.

You're idiotic, you are! She lay looking up at the plaster rose in the ceiling from which was appended a delicately beautiful chandelier. The bedroom was on the grand scale, from another age, the bed, a mahogany fourposter undraped for coolness, the twin set of French doors that led out on to the verandah shuttered in dark green and fitted with full-length sliding insect screens, a must for the tropics and dispensing with en-veloping mosquito netting. Yesterday morning Susan had been too weak and stunned to take in much of her surroundings beyond the large scale of the house and a grandeur she wasn't used to, but last night she had had to fight not to appear overawed. The Chandler who had built this house must have planned everything down to the last detail and he had been very lavish with his money. It had been built high off the ground with splendid verandahs and strong enough to withstand the most battering cyclone.

She felt happy. She had decided not to worry and obviously Jeff craved the excitement of staying on Lara for a while. It would have been asking too much for Felicia to welcome her. Felicia appeared to feel nothing for anyone except her immediate family. Susan set her teeth in her full lower lip. Even if she had mistaken the quality of all those dark, devouring glances, she hadn't mistaken seeing them walking together in the garden, long after she had excused herself for the night—Felicia, a tall woman, made small by her brother-in-law's height and breadth of shoulder. They had come to a halt in the shining moonlight and Susan had seen Felicia reach up swiftly and put her hands to those same wide shoulders she had clung to herself. What happened next Susan couldn't bear to see. She had turned away flushed and ashamed, incapable of witnessing Felicia's complete surrender to the emotional storm that was undoubtedly in her. It was easy to understand the gossip now. Felicia Chandler looked at her brother-in-law like a lover. Not that Susan could blame her even if it troubled and upset her so strangely. It was so easy to conjure him up at will. He was too damned attractive, enough to knock the wind out of any woman's sails—even a *femme du monde* like Felicia.

Susan got up and put on the blue robe, then walked to the screened doors and opened them up. The garden was splendid, a tropical paradise; the great poincianas in brilliant colour, dropping scarlet blossoms with the whim of the breeze; the dazzling yellow gold of the cascaras and cassias, the smaller trees, the oleanders and frangipani of wonderful fragrance and every conceivable tint. There was even an avenue of coconut palms that bore prolifically. It all looked incredibly lush, unfamiliar, and she began to understand Jeff's craving for release from conformity and an ordinary everyday existence. The North was very generous with its beauty. It slipped out everywhere in tropical profusion.

For a moment she stood there listening to the blissful chirruping and warbling and screeching of the birds, then she went back and sat on the edge of the bed wondering what to wear. She hadn't looked so bad last night. She recalled every minute of it—how the talk had flowed effortlessly between Devin Chandler and his sister-in-law, how he had laughed at her witty, faintly malicious observations. They looked good together, both Beautiful People. Susan thought no more about them, but decided on a blue and white cotton shirt and narrow jeans. Jill was as slender and spare as herself, though everything did up very easily with her weight loss.

Later, as she was thinking of exploring the garden, the French doors along the verandah opened out and a little girl emerged somewhat furtively to gaze in Susan's direction.

'Hello there!' The child had nothing of her mother's beautiful appearance or the powerfully classic good looks of her uncle.

The child didn't answer but broke off a choked little exclamation and hurried back into her room.

'Oh dear!' Susan gave a doubtful little sigh. Teaching had given her, at least to children, a gentle air of authority and she decided to move further down the verandah, not to intrude on the child's privacy but perhaps coax her out again.

'It's all right, Emma,' she called. 'I only wanted to ask you if you would show me the garden. It's so big, it would be better to walk with someone who knows it.'

No movement inside the bedroom, then a faint stirring.

'Please come out, Emma,' Susan asked softly, 'there's so many things I'd like to ask you. The birds make a din, don't they? There's a parrot right here now. I think it might be a Golden-shoulder.'

'*No!*'

It was Susan's first real look at the child. She emerged to stand just outside the French doors, a white, strained little face, dark hair, dark eyes, a thin little body like a bundle of sticks. There was a short silence until she managed more, staring up at Susan as though despite herself she approved her.

'The Golden-shoulder is quite rare. You could spend weeks trying to sight one unless you moved up into the Peninsula.'

'I've been told they're magnificent?'

'Yes, and terrible people, bird dealers, trap them then drug them and sell them overseas.'

'How awful!' Susan drew in her breath and made a sound of disgust.

'I've known that for ages,' Emma added, almost tolerantly. 'Aren't you a teacher? You're supposed to be clever.' She eyed Susan with great dark eyes that seemed to miss nothing.

'Mind you, I generally am,' Susan said lightly, and smiled. 'Having lived up here you'd know so many interesting things. I'm glad our paths crossed.'

Emma stared back as if puzzled. 'Tell me how you got yourself lost. Mother said you must be quite mad to think you could go for an idle stroll through the jungle.'

'Even so,' said Susan, 'in a strange way, it was an experience I'll remember all my life. The rain forest is so beautiful, so wonderfully exotic with the ferns and the orchids and all the other plants that cover the trees.'

'Epiphytes!' Emma nodded her head knowledgeably, a faint flush making her skin less pale. 'It's all the constant moisture. There used to be rain forests everywhere in my grandfather's time, now there are dairy farms and canefields and cattle stations like Lara.' Her high, narrow forehead was covered in a fringe that made her large dark eyes appear, if anything, more wary. 'Weren't you frightened at night?' she asked Susan as though expecting her to lie.

'Yes, very!' Susan gave an unforced shudder. 'One moment it was dusk, then complete darkness....'

'Don't talk about it if you don't want to.' Emma darted another glance at her. 'I think you were awfully brave.'

'I suppose that's because you're very kind.'

'No, not exactly.' Emma pushed her long limp dark hair back over her shoulder. 'I just know what it's like to be frightened. Haven't you got the most super coloured hair?'

'Do you really think so?' Spontaneously Susan put out her hand and apparently without thinking the child took it, allowing herself to be drawn down the verandah and out into the garden. 'I used to get an awful lot of teasing at school, which is what one expects with red hair, but now I've grown up it's darkened a lot. At your age, it used to be a radiant red.'

'Mother's hair used to be the same colour as mine,' Emma supplied, and her voice sounded utterly drained of vitality. 'I think it's ridiculous to dye your hair, but she prefers it that way.'

'She's very beautiful!' Susan murmured, lifting her face to the warm, scented breeze.

'I'm sure you like Uncle Dev?' Emma asked, and lifted her young-old eyes.

'I'm afraid without Uncle Dev, dear, I mightn't be here,' Susan answered. 'You see, not only did I lose myself, but a wild boar attacked me.'

'Really?' Emma looked her amazement. 'Mother doesn't know about it.'

'Probably your uncle didn't want to disturb her, but the incident was real. The boar rushed me and your uncle had to kill it. I made a fool of myself as well—I just screamed and screamed.'

'You lost control?' Emma spoke to her quite kindly.

'I'll say I did!' Susan bent down and picked up a frangipani flower and twirled it idly under her nose. 'I just wanted to hide.'

Emma didn't answer immediately, her plain little face inscrutable as a Buddha, then she sighed. 'It might sound pretty funny, but sometimes I want to hide too.'

'That's understandable.' Susan walked on, trying not to be obvious. Emma wouldn't like pity and though she wasn't a happy child she appeared to have no difficulty communicating with a stranger. 'Don't imagine grown-ups don't feel like that sometimes. Life can be difficult, not all peace and content.'

'No,' Emma sighed.

At this point Susan decided to change the conversation. As a child psychologist she wasn't all that bad and already Emma had taken to her. She began to ask questions about the different trees and shrubs, humouring the little girl, letting her show off her knowledge. Everything seemed to be in flower and the display was brilliant.

The morning was warming and as they came back towards the house with Emma identifying three species of birds unique to the North, the child suddenly grasped her hand. 'Mother said you'd be going away today.'

'I don't have to.' Susan came to a halt, looking down into the girl's eyes. 'Your uncle has asked me to stay on for a little while as his guest.'

'Why don't you?' Emma didn't smile, but Susan's answered seemed to be important to her.

'As a matter of fact, I'd like to. I don't know nearly as much about this part of the world as you.'

'Oh, it's beautiful, I tell you. Beautiful!' Emma jerked her head in the direction of the magnificent lagoon just that bit far for them to walk to. 'There are so many things I could show you.'

'All right, then, I'd enjoy that.'

'Really?' From intensity Emma gave way to listlessness. 'Mother says I'm not the least bit interesting.'

'I'm sure she didn't say that, Emma,' Susan couldn't refrain from correcting her.

'Not to me,' Emma answered dully, 'but in my hearing. Actually she's right. I mostly act like an imbecile.'

'You mean you're sometimes not in the mood to laugh and smile?'

'Not in a long while!' Emma squinted against the brilliant sunlight.

'Well, I'm glad to say I find you very interesting,' Susan maintained gallantly. 'And very observant. I'm sure you could teach me a lot.'

They were approaching the house and Susan stopped still, the better to enjoy it. 'I've seen plenty of houses—plenty, but I've never seen one like this.'

'We're rich,' Emma answered matter-of-factly. 'Aren't you?'

'Far from it,' Susan told her cheerfully. 'No one makes a fortune teaching school, but I enjoy it.'

'I'm going to a boarding school at the end of the holidays,' Emma said with her eyes on her clenched hands.

'You don't sound as if you're looking forward to it?'

'I hate to be cooped up.' Emma's dark eyes searched Susan's face. 'I've just thought I could ask Mother to send me to *your* school. At least someone would know me.'

Susan spoke to her calmly, though she could see the child was utterly miserable. 'Even though you don't think so now, dear, boarding school can be fun. There are all the other girls and you could make a lot of friends.'

'*Never!*' Emma answered brokenly, and ran off before Susan could say another word.

Susan surged after her, her tender heart rocking. Poor little Emma! They both knew she would never be one to make friends easily, and the naked pain in the child's large dark eyes had shocked her.

Only a crisis stopped Emma's flying feet. As she reached the verandah, her eyes blurred with tears, she heard clearly the pitiful wail of a kitten that swept her own unhappiness away from her completely. Susan had reached her and she turned her white face towards her.

'*Listen!*'

Susan dropped into a planter's chair, her dark red curls damp at the temples. 'You won't have any trouble with field and track. You move like a rocket.'

'It's one of the kittens.' Emma moved towards her. 'May I call you Susan?'

'Sure. I've been calling you Emma.'

Emma's hand pulled at her urgently, forcing her up. 'I think the poor foolish little thing is caught up a tree.'

'Where?' Immediately Susan straightened her drooping shoulders.

'There!' Emma cried in a wild little voice. 'How did

it get up there? I can't stand it!'

It would have been funny, only the child was so up-set. 'I see it now,' Susan panted, still a little dazed from her run in the hot sun. 'I expect it decided on a little adventure, but going up wasn't as difficult as com-ing down.'

The sweat had broken out on Emma's clammy little face. 'If you don't rescue it, it will be dead!'

'Don't be ridiculous!' For a moment Susan stared at the child, though she didn't dare laugh at her. 'You know the old story since long before the Pharaohs. Cats have nine lives.'

'It's Sweetie, and she's used up a lot of them,' Emma protested. She was trembling from head to foot and Susan looked back at her trying to understand.

'Then we'd just better rescue her. I expect she's pretty much in control of things, but I don't like to see you so upset. Believe me, dear, I've lived with cats all my life.'

'*Please!*' Emma whispered in a flat little voice.

'Right!' In a few seconds Susan was up on the verandah railing and from there she propelled herself into the big, beautiful shade tree that spread its sturdy branches towards the side of the house. The kitten, a tawny little thing with yellow eyes and interrupted stripes, gave every appearance of being frozen to a branch much higher up.

'Sweetie!' Susan called to her, feeling very much out of practice at rescuing cats.

The kitten saw her, but insisted on staying where it was, its bushy tail straight up.

So I'm faced with a problem! Susan thought. Nimbly she climbed further up the tree, prepared to have the kitten scratch her before it allowed itself to be dragged down from its lofty perch. Instead it proceeded to pick its way delicately towards her until she was able to pick it up with one hand and continue back down the tree. It was just as she had said, cats for the most part knew exactly how to take good care of themselves—in fact the kitten was now objecting to being rescued at all.

Nearing the lower branches it insisted on jumping and just as Susan decided it needed its claws trimmed a branch snapped in her hands and as she swung out for another, her foot slipped and she fell out of the tree into the grass below.

In a panic Emma ran to her, calling her name, but Susan was in no condition to answer her. She was winded and Emma looked down at her, terrified she was badly hurt.

'Emma!' Uncle Devin was behind her, lifting her bodily out of the way. 'My God!' he looked down at Susan as though he found it difficult to believe his eyes.

'She fell out of the tree.' Emma's thin little face looked ghastly with shock.

'This is too much!' Her uncle set his white teeth, his hands running deftly over Susan's slender limbs. 'In fact it's crazy. What in God's name was she doing up a tree?'

'Rescuing Sweetie!' Emma's frail breast rose and fell agitatedly under her thin cotton shirt.

'It's all right!' Susan opened her eyes, the brief moments of pain over. 'I haven't climbed a tree in years.'

'Lie still.' He looked at her reprovingly, his eyes

glittery and narrow in a dark, grim face. 'I haven't known you very long, but I don't trust you out of my sight.'

'It's my fault!' wailed Emma.

'For goodness' sake, there's nothing wrong with me!' Susan grasped hold of the child's hand and pulled her down on to the grass. 'I'll guarantee you one thing— Sweetie got clean away.'

'She did.'

'Beautiful!' Susan flung her arm out, content to lie in the warm, scented grass.

'It's a good thing youngsters mend easily.' The green eyes skimmed her body intently. In every way intent. No matter how she acted something about the way she looked pleased him. It was just incredible. She couldn't believe it.

'Dev! What's going on there?' Felicia was swaying down the length of the verandah, staring down at them. '*Dev?*' she addressed him directly, all the honey drained out of her tone.

'Susan, do you think you can get up now?' He turned his dark head to her, his voice crisp and bracing.

'Sure. I'm fine.'

Emma, full of equal parts of relief and contrition, moved to her assistance, only her uncle grasped Susan firmly and lifted her to her feet. 'Next time you see a kitten in distress, call me and mind your own business.'

'Yes, sir. Whatever you say, I'll take it very seriously.'

'Don't tell me Susan's had another accident?' Even at that hour Felicia was perfectly made up, though she still wore an entrancing peignoir.

'That's right!' Susan smiled, conscious of the child

standing stiffly beside her. 'It seems to be the normal sort of thing for me lately.'

'Emma!' Felicia spoke to her daughter and Susan wondered whether she knew it sounded like a bark. 'Come in now and have your breakfast.'

'Come with me?' Emma looked up at Susan with the question.

'Susan will be there in a minute,' her uncle told her. 'Go along like a good girl or it will soon be lunch time.'

Up on the verandah Felicia stood over her daughter for a moment, then shepherded her inside, flashing one last glance over her shoulder at her brother-in-law and the silent girl at his side.

'How did you do it?' he asked her.

'My foot slipped.'

'Oh God, I'm talking about Emma,' he bit off. 'You've reached her already.'

'Here's the odd thing,' Susan returned wryly, 'unlike you, she accepts me.'

'You're here. I must accept you,' he said with a faint glimmer of amusement in his voice.

'So it looks like I'm staying.'

'Don't be sorry.' He lifted her chin, forcing her to look at him.

'For Emma.' She was actually aware of his fingers against her skin, the dark green eyes studying her.

'Of course. You're a nice child. I thought they'd gone out of existence.'

CHAPTER THREE

In the following days, the time passed very quickly. The Conrads had arrived and though Susan found them very friendly and nice, she had no wish to try and push herself in where she didn't belong. She couldn't even consider herself a guest in the real sense, after all, the Chandlers didn't even know her, but her friendship with Emma developed very swiftly.

While Felicia played hostess, entertaining Trish Conrad, and the men, deep in conversation, went everywhere about the property together, Susan and Emma passed their days very pleasantly. Though they weren't allowed to stray very far into the magnificent countryside there were many beautiful spots close enough in to the house that they could visit, and none more welcome in the brilliant heat than the lagoon; as cool and green and sheltered as a forest pool.

'This is lovely, isn't it?' Emma dashed herself with cold water, then fell with a splash into the water.

Perched on a rock, Susan smiled at the thin little figure, noting with satisfaction that Emma's swimming had improved with a few lessons and her white skin had acquired an enhancing tan.

'Aren't you coming in?' Emma stood under the sparkling cascades that dashed over the high boulders.

'In a minute.' Susan settled the picnic basket high up and away from the ants, then she peeled off her dress, walking unselfconsciously in her brief two-piece swim-suit down the mossy bank and into the beautifully clear water. Her hair she had gathered on top of her head and as Emma watched her she struck out stylishly to-wards the miniature waterfall.

'You're awfully good, aren't you?' Emma said ad-miringly.

'Good enough. What about you? You've come along a lot this week.'

'I know that, because you've helped me. Promise me you'll stay my friend.'

'Emma, love....' In that beautiful, tranquil setting Susan heard the sad, ragged note of the child's voice.

'Before I go to bed I always say a prayer we'll be friends for ever. Promise you won't laugh?'

'Who's laughing?' Susan spoke soothingly, such a gentle expression on her lovely young face that the child seemed healed.

'A pity we're not sisters. I always wanted a sister. Some day Daddy said I would have one, but then he died.'

It was the first time Emma had ever mentioned her father and Susan drew close to her as they trod water together.

'But you have such good memories of him, don't you, dear?'

'You try it. Try losing your father!' Emma suddenly shouted, and struck out for the opposite bank.

Susan was almost immediately beside her, strained and urgent. 'Go easy, dear. You won't make the dis-tance.'

'Oh, *help* me!' Emma's dark eyes looked frantic, the cry wrenched from the heart.

'Relax. I've got you. Go on, relax!'

But some deep emotion was exploding in Emma. Instead of allowing Susan to bring her in, she began struggling, rejecting Susan fiercely. 'Let me *go*!'

'That's enough!' Susan laboured to hold on to the child. 'And stop screaming. It doesn't help one bit.'

By the time she finally got Emma to the bank, she lay back exhausted, with the child lying on her side beside her, weeping bitterly.

When she was able, Susan laid her hand on the little girl's shoulder, then when Emma didn't reject her she drew the small shuddering body into her arms. 'There now ... there now. Understand you have a friend.'

Hunched in Susan's arms, Emma's thin frame was racked with sobs, but instead of stopping her, Susan's soft murmurs and her gentle hand in the child's hair encouraged her to cry out. 'Why didn't I die with Daddy? I wanted to!'

'Darling,' Susan's compassionate heart smote her, 'everyone is so glad you're alive. You know your father would never have let you die. He gave you life and he wants you to live it fully.'

'I didn't mean to hurt you back there.' Emma lifted her head, her small face blotched and swollen with weeping.

'I know.' Susan smoothed back the wet fringe from Emma's forehead. 'How do you feel?'

'Terrible. I don't see, Susan, why fathers have to die.'

'That's exactly the way I felt when my mother died.' Susan drew the child to her. 'Scared too and terribly lonely. My mother was someone special. I didn't think God would allow it.'

'But He did.'

'Yes, dear, that was His way, though I don't understand it. Maybe it's being very selfish. I'm sure my mother is very happy right now.'

'Yes, but we can't *see* them!' Emma insisted.

'No, that's the terrible thing, but they can see us. Above anything else you would want your father to be proud of you, wouldn't you?'

'He was the only person who truly loved me.' For a devastating moment Emma sounded as perceptive and intelligent as any adult.

'But your mother loves you,' Susan protested, disturbed.

'Honestly, she doesn't.' Emma compressed her colourless lips. 'She swore she wasn't going to have another baby because it would ruin her figure. She was always saying terrible things to Daddy—about the family, Uncle Dev. She called Daddy her biggest mistake. I used to hear all the arguments. I used to creep down the hallway instead of going to bed.'

'And of course you heard a lot of things you didn't really understand.'

Emma frowned, trying to remember. 'Do you think Mummy really wanted to marry Uncle Dev?'

'I'm sure she deeply loved your father,' Susan answered without hesitation, though she couldn't help sharing Emma's dismay. 'It's just that it's natural for people who love each other to have arguments from time to time. It clears the air. I'm sure your parents wouldn't have had them, had they known they had an audience.'

'Do you think so? *I* don't!' Emma sighed deeply. 'Uncle Dev's like a stranger these days, now that Daddy's gone.'

'He has a deep affection for you, Emma.' Susan said this with no feeling of hypocrisy. She knew by now, Devin Chandler did care about the child.

'Maybe it's pretending,' Emma said with an exhausted air. 'What am I anyway, a no-no. I completely missed out on Mummy's looks.'

'How do *you* know?' Susan demanded, clasping the child's face. 'You don't believe you're going to stay the same for ever? You're going to fill out and blossom and you have striking eyes.'

Though she was much agitated, Emma visibly brightened. With an immense effort she smiled, her drying hair falling all over her cheeks. 'And you, of course, were a perfectly beautiful baby. You should see Minna's baby. It's adorable!'

Susan regarded the child with approval, then she leaned over and kissed her cheek. 'It's going to be all right, Emma,' she promised.

Jeff had been invited up to dinner on the Conrads' last evening along with Rick Gardiner, a young man about Jeff's age, who was having a year on Lara gaining valuable experience before taking over the management of a small family holding. He was bright, eager, with a faint air of arrogance, and it was obvious from the way he sat there studying Susan that he liked her looks, at least.

The talk at the dinner table flourished, with Bob Conrad telling them all about the wonderful, adventurous times he had had with Dev from the time they were boys, while Devin Chandler shook his head, faintly smiling. He was seated at the head of the long, gleaming table with Felicia focusing all her attention on him from the other end, Susan seated opposite Rick with Jeff beside her and the Conrads nearest their host. Mrs Hansen's cooking was in the Cordon Bleu class and the table was beautifully laid, almost a star attraction on its own.

'No beef like Lara beef!' Bob Conrad maintained, finishing off a succulent pepper steak. He turned to Susan, continuing to ask her questions with interest. He was a very vital man in a different way from his great friend and Susan had the impression he kept a mental catalogue with file cards on every person he met. 'I guess you've seen more of the country now than most people, Susan, but you've yet to explore the beauties of the Great Barrier Reef.'

'Book us all into your hotel,' Felicia suggested smoothly.

'Why not? It sounds like a great idea!' Bob Conrad seemed genuinely pleased with the idea. 'It's a great place. Isn't that right, Dev?'

'If I didn't live here, I'd live there!' He turned his dark head and smiled at Bob's wife.

'Not you!' Trish asserted definitely. 'It's from Lara you draw your great strength.'

'I'll say!' Bob Conrad gave them an all-engulfing smile. 'Running Lara is like running one's own country. With Dev for a friend I was determined one day I'd make it as well. You might say he dragged me along with him until I had no place to go but the top of the tree.'

'Not entirely,' Devin Chandler interrupted. 'All I did was open a few doors.'

'More than that, son!' Bob Conrad shook his heavy, sun-bleached head. 'You and your dad made me over entirely. It's unbelievable. Even as a kid you were making decisions, acting in a particular way. I wanted to be the same.'

'Accept it, Dev!' Trish Conrad smiled at her host with warmth and affection. 'You had a great deal to do with Bob's success.'

While the men talked of the good times and the bad, the opening up of a wild, untamed land, Susan took stock of her brother's expression. He was hanging on every word as though these stories of the far North were magic. Jeff, too, had ambition and a thirst for adventure and only a few days ago Devin Chandler had told Susan her brother was 'coming along extremely well'. Now he was looking at his boss with an expression Susan had never seen, a kind of hero-worship and an insatiable desire to work and own a small part of this world. Felicia treated him in a patronising manner, although curiously she seemed to approve his undeniable good looks, but these days for Jeff, Devin Chandler was absolutely splendid. Few lived the way he did, with so much land and power, so Jeff worked hard and listened and hungrily drank in all the glorious sights and sounds and smells of a great Run. Lara was an empire and Devin Chandler was a brilliant and extraordinary man.

If Felicia felt indignant at having Susan so unexpectedly included in the Conrads' invitation, she didn't show it. Apparently both Bob and Trish found the girl appealing, so whatever her private thoughts, Felicia pulled herself up smartly. Trish Conrad was smiling at Susan, explaining that there was an airstrip on Sunset, one of the prettiest and best served of all the Barrier Reef islands, and how proud they were of the fine hotel Bob's company had built on the richly wooded emerald island.

'It's very kind of you to ask me,' Susan smiled, warming to the older woman's charm.

'Now we'll have to decide when Dev can fly you over.'

'I wish someone would wave an invitation at me,' Rick Gardiner lamented, his light blue eyes raking every inch of Susan that was visible. 'Jeff mightn't be able to get away, but I've a few free weekends up my sleeve. Sunset is a beautiful place to relax and when you haven't time to show Susan around, I'll be there waiting.'

'Don't bother to make a reservation,' Devin Chandler told him smoothly. 'That's all news to me, those free weekends. You're high up on my wanted list.'

'Drat it!' Rick returned a little flatly, then because everyone was looking at him he smiled. 'It was just that it would give me great pleasure to show Susan my part of the world.'

'Yes,' Devin Chandler answered, and that seemed to be the end of it.

Each time Susan looked up after that, Rick seemed to be staring at her and she found it faintly embarrassing. Felicia and Trish Conrad, both very attractive women, might not have existed, but then, of course, she was the only woman eligible at the dinner table. She couldn't have said why, Rick was attractive and well bred, apart from the unnecessary staring, but she didn't like him. Nor did she wish him to find her attractive.

The evening came to a very pleasant close and Susan walked down the verandah stairs with her brother.

'I think Rick fell in love with you on sight,' Jeff said almost absently. 'No wonder!'

'I don't know that I altogether like him,' Susan said, flustered. The light shone on her, on her hair and her dress and her skin, and she looked very young and lovely and not quite a woman.

'That was a wonderful evening!' Jeff said enthusiastically, and took his sister's arm. 'I don't expect I'll get another invitation up to the house again, but that will do me all my life.'

'You want to stay, then?' Susan asked, feeling suddenly very lonely and deserted.

'I want time, love. There's so much to do and see. Can't you understand that?'

'Of course I can.' Above them the night sky was lit with the brilliance of stars, the air heavily scented with the exotic blooms of the tropics. 'I wish I could share your life, but a woman doesn't enjoy the same freedom as a man. A woman has to be properly housed and protected. Devin Chandler would want me away from here anyway.'

'But, sweetie, he's treating you royally.'

'I know!' A night bird flew overhead with a movement of wings. 'I sometimes dream I'm back in the rain forest opening my eyes. I owe him my life.'

'Don't remind me!' Jeff transferred his arm to his sister's shoulder, hugging her. 'Do you know what he calls you?'

'He has a name for me?' Susan looked up at her brother in astonishment.

'Blue Lotus!' Jeff tilted his sister's chin. 'You know what he's like. He's a very responsible man. He won't let you go until he's sure you're quite well again. Oh, I don't mean physically,' Jeff held her firmly as she stirred restively, 'but mentally as well. That was a terrifying experience, I know, I had a little of it as well, and you said yourself you're still having nightmares.'

'Why Blue Lotus?' she asked in a strained little voice.

'You have violet eyes, don't you remember?'

'Oh!' Her sigh fell gently. 'He's not by nature a patient man and I don't want to be a clinging vine. I must go home—not that we've had a home since Mummy died.'

'No,' Jeff said quietly, but Susan could feel the tension in him. 'How did Dad ever get mixed up with a phoney like Pamela?'

'She loves him. You know it. She's very clever with Dad. We were the ones that made difficulties, complicated her life. I'm sure she's happy now with Dad all to herself.'

'You'd better write to him.'

'I *have*. So should you,' Susan said, unable to stop herself.

'Sorry, love, don't try to live my life for me. After Dad married Pamela we ceased to exist as a family. And it wasn't all Pamela's fault. Dad never did try to understand me. You were his precious little girl, but I was something else, almost a problem. From the time Mum died, Dad and I were never close. I was glad to leave really.'

'I'm rather afraid you hurt Dad as well,' Susan declared sadly. 'He does love you, Jeff.'

'Like the beautiful icy Felicia loves that poor little kid, I suppose?'

'That's none of our business....'

'Why not?' Jeff asked a little heatedly. 'She's got you acting nursemaid.'

'You don't understand,' Susan answered quietly, 'she's a very nice little girl. I've become fond of her and I want to help her.'

'Well, everyone agrees she needs it!' Jeff sounded impatient. 'You might be able to handle the kid all right, but it would surprise me just to see her open her mouth. She wanders around the place like a little wraith.'

'That's because she doesn't know how to cope with her despair. She adored her father, and her mother does seem a little distant....'

'If you ask me,' Jeff interrupted fiercely, 'she's desperately trying to be Mrs *Devin* Chandler.'

'She's very beautiful,' Susan heard herself say.

'She's that!' Jeff agreed tersely. 'I wonder what kind of man would warm her? I can't see her with Chandler somehow. A man like that is a natural born hunter. *He'd* pick the woman, and it's my guess she'd be Felicia's opposite in every way.'

'You're not attracted to her, are you?' Susan demanded, dismayed by a telling note in her brother's voice.

'Oh, God!' Jeff mumbled impatiently, and his eyes flashed back to the big, rambling white house. 'She doesn't know I'm alive, let alone give me the chance to speak to her.'

'Jeff!' In those moments of stunned silence, Susan was glad of the dark. She was totally shocked at the very idea of Jeff being interested in Felicia, even if that lady scarcely knew he existed. There was no room in Felicia's life for nobodies, and Lara's employees were barely more than a blur. There could be no joy whatever in Jeff's becoming infatuated with a classic, cold beauty like Felicia Chandler. The description Susan considered a good one. Felicia had barely glanced at Jeff right through the evening. Perhaps that was precisely the challenge. Jeff had always had plenty of girl-friends at his beck and call. Now he was painfully aware that the rich, sophisticated sort didn't even see him.

'Let's forget it!' Jeff's blue eyes turned expressionless. 'I'm not going to make a fool of myself, Susie!'

'I'm delighted to hear it.' As she answered Susan wondered exactly what her brother had in mind. He had become very used to easy conquests that required no more than good looks and an engaging, slightly raffish manner, now he was suddenly unsure of his own attraction.

After they had said goodnight, Susan lingered in the garden, blending with the shadows. She hadn't wanted to wound her brother by pointing out the enormous difference in the life style of the Chandlers and the Conrads compared with their own comfortable but ordinary background. There might be beauty, danger and romance on Lara, but there was also the possibility of humiliation and pain. A woman who could be cruel to her own child wouldn't concern herself with deliberately impressing a susceptible young man simply to feel her own power. Appearing neither to have heard nor seen him, Felicia might already have read the secret message in Jeff's eyes.

'Susan?'

In the darkness Susan couldn't see Devin Chandler's tall, muscular frame, but she would know his voice anywhere.

'Over here.'

'Keep talking!' he commanded, and she could hear the faint smile in his mocking, indulgent tone.

'Here.'

'That's it!' he said, and took her arm, moving so silently he was towering over her even as she turned her head in slight agitation. 'What are you doing out here in the dark?'

'Thinking.'

'I see. What about?'

'Nothing serious.' She took a deep breath. 'I want to thank you for inviting Jeff up to dinner.'

'He was here because he's your brother and I knew it would please you.'

'Surely he made a contribution,' she retorted. 'He hung on your every word.'

'What a pity that wasn't true of you.' His voice mocked her. 'If I were you I wouldn't give young Gardiner the slightest encouragement. He's here to gain experience, but only in the business.'

'Of course you're joking?' She lifted her clear, deep eyes.

'No, I'm not. Not tonight. Not tomorrow and however long you're on the property. From the way Rick was looking at you, a pleasant, uncomplicated friendship is out of the question. I'm sure if you were a little more experienced you would have to agree.'

'I'm a lot more grown up than Emma!' She flashed him another look, her cheeks burning.

'Do you think so?' he teased. 'What is it, anyway? Something's distressing you.'

'I just have the dreadful feeling I'm imposing on you,' she sighed.

'You never give up, do you?' he asked almost tolerantly. 'Actually, little one, I owe you a lot. Emma's happiness means a great deal to me and you're doing more than any of us to bring her out.'

'It might take a long time.' The soft night air lifted her hair and blew it about her small face.

'Would it help if I offered you a job?' he asked a little curtly, 'Seeing you're plainly unhappy as my guest.'

'I want to go home.' She shook her hair back a little fiercely, mortified that she was so intensely, physically aware of him.

'Why so frightened?' His voice flicked at her. 'Your brother told me neither of you had really had a home since your mother died.'

'I hope he told you as well that I love my father very dearly.'

'And he you. You know damned well I've spoken to him.' He put out his hands and shook her slightly. 'You're wound up about more than that.'

You, she thought wildly, her whole body vibrating. What was the matter with her worrying about Jeff when her own emotions were even more ludicrous under the circumstances?

'Let's walk a way, shall we?' He turned her gently by her drooping shoulder, while her thin blue dress blew back from her slender body. 'You find life a little too much for you sometimes, don't you, Susan?'

'Yes, I do.' She stumbled and he caught her arm. 'You must think I'm a fool.'

'I think you're completely unawakened—almost an anachronism in this day and age. Girls as beautiful as you are usually well armed against life, full of a natural self-confidence. You have rather a haunting little way about you, a naked vulnerability. Don't be angry with me if I find it touching.'

'But you don't approve.' It was a statement, not a question, and it sounded a little forlorn.

'Does it matter to you?' he asked.

'You know, emotionally, I feel I owe you a great deal.'

'Then pay me,' he said, in a hard, controlled voice. 'Everyone else has been a failure with Emma, but you. Maybe it's because you're not quite grown up yourself.'

'I'm twenty-two!' she protested.

'No matter. It's not just a question of birthdays. Emma enjoys being with you. You make her feel safe and wanted and so far as I'm concerned she can try to copy you to her heart's content. Everything about you fits the way you look.'

'You know she hates the idea of boarding school?'

'Doesn't everyone?' he asked dryly. 'I loathed every minute I spent away from Lara.'

'Emma may be your niece, but she's not in the least like you,' commented Susan. 'I'm sure she was always a locked-in child.'

'Never as silent and withdrawn as she's been since Brad died. He was always very important to her, though in those days she used to sit in my lap when her father wasn't available. Somehow I've turned into a bogey when she should feel closer to her family.'

'Your brother didn't live on Lara?' she asked him quietly.

'He lived with my mother until he married,' he answered with hard directness. 'My mother is a highly intelligent and very striking looking woman, but unlike you, she found the North more alien than colourful. Her brother, my Uncle David, was drowned on the property as a young man. He was thrown from his horse in a flash flood and swept away in the flood waters. He was found a few days later wedged in the fork of a tree. She never got over it, nor the fear of death and danger. She was certain one of her sons had to die. Life on a big cattle station can be violent and there's always the threat of devastation from tropical cyclones. She was determined one of us would be spared, but my father was a powerful man. In the end, after much bitterness, he consented to letting her have Brad providing he spent his every vacation on Lara. I was eleven and Brad was seven.'

'So you rarely saw your mother?' some powerful urge made her ask.

'She didn't want to see *me*,' he answered coolly.

'Perhaps she couldn't cope with the pain.'

He shook his arrogant dark head. 'She didn't want me. Only Brad. Now look at how things have turned out! My father is gone; he threw his life away, and Brad finished his life in a plane crash. I've always had this infernal feeling it was my fault. He was always trying to do something to please me. However little we'd seen of each other we were very close. He was my younger brother and he was flying back to give me the results of a meeting I'd already heard about. He was new to everything—big business, negotiations, but his motives were always excellent. My mother found it unforgivable the close communication between us and the fact that I wanted him to help me run Lara. Damn it all, he was part of it. Lara was his heritage as well, though my father only left him a considerable sum of money.' He lifted his hand and let it fall on Susan's delicate, sloping shoulder. 'Why am I telling you all this?'

'I asked.'

'Yes,' he admitted, 'but I'm not usually so forthcoming.'

'It's a very tragic story.'

'Don't break your tender little heart on me,' he laughed a little harshly.

'I can't, and I *won't*!' She was terrified of her own feelings, the strength in the fingers closed around her arm, his overriding physical attraction for her.

'What is that supposed to mean?' The hard note in his voice turned to amused mockery.

She could have killed herself for saying it, for so transparently revealing her own terribly unsophisticated emotions. It was just as Felicia had implied she was no more than a gauche schoolgirl helplessly falling in love with a hard, dazzling, confident man. The whole thing made her shaky with self humiliation.

A fruit bat flew past overhead, zooming so low towards the magnificently plump ripe mangoes that Susan gave a strangled little cry and put her hands over her head.

'What's wrong with you?' He pushed her curly head against his shoulder. 'You don't have to get into this sort of a pickle about a harmless little bat. It's the mangoes it's after, not you.'

'I don't think I'll ever get over being lost. Ever.'

'I think you've handled it all right.' Abruptly he freed her and drew her back towards the house.

'I keep remembering the way I crammed berries into my mouth. They tasted bitter-sweet and the juice was pink. I was going to try to dry them. Then when I thought about really starving I tried to look for edible roots. I knew the natives ate lily bulbs and wild plants.'

'The miracle was you didn't eat something that would have made you terribly sick or high. There's a particular little bush with bright red berries that the old medicine men used to use as a potent drug,' he told her dryly.

'It's such a strange feeling to be totally alone,' Susan found herself saying. 'When I rested I used to go over all my childhood memories—my mother mostly. She came back so vividly to me. There was nothing else around me but the great trees and the vines.' Her voice was low and unsteady.

'Stop it, little one,' he touched her bare arm.

'I'm sorry!' She turned her head and the lights from the house caught her shimmering, wide open eyes. 'I'm not very good at coping either.'

'It's over,' he said quietly, looking down at her. 'I'll take you back to the rain forest. In daylight. You'll be quite safe and I'll teach you how to save your life.'

'I don't expect *you* to continue to save it,' she said with a little broken laugh.

'Are you sleeping well?' He drew her still further into the light, obviously intent on finding out the answer to his question.

'Oh, yes,' she tried to smile at him. 'Coming North seems to have changed the whole course of our lives. Jeff's and mine. He wants to remain on Lara.'

'I know.' His voice was calm but clearly authoritative. 'There's a place for him and he's shown he knows how to make himself useful. The North needs young men, thousands of them. At this point your brother is working himself out.'

'Whereas I have to go home without him.'

'It shouldn't be long before you're married,' his green eyes were steady on her face. 'Your brother must live his own life.'

'So go ahead, take him away from me!' she said emotionally.

'I know he's important to you,' he said, frowning, 'but you can't let yourself become dependent on him.'

'Didn't I tell you I'm a teacher?' Her creamy skin was flushing and there was the shimmer of tears in her eyes.

'And I don't doubt a good one, but that's not what we're talking about. I don't want to hurt you.'

'I think you do.' She avoided his brilliant, analytical glance.

'When you're stronger I'll make you apologise for that.'

'Oh, anything!' She turned away from him, distracted, running up the short flight of steps to the verandah in an urgent hurry to get away.

Felicia was half way through the open doorway and her dark glance struck Susan's flushed and tense little face. 'You seem to have been gone a long time?'

'I wanted a breath of fresh air.'

Felicia looked beyond her down towards the pool of

light at the base of the stairs. Devin Chandler stood there, in perfect control of his hard powerful body and his emotions.

'Oh, there you are, darling!' Her high voice cut into the dark, scented night. 'You're full of surprises. I'd no idea where you got to.'

'I keep telling you, Flick,' he smiled at her, 'that's what makes being a bachelor so pleasant. I've no woman to answer to.'

'Falling in love happens suddenly!' she answered triumphantly, and held out her hand to him. 'Trish wants to know if we're going to fly over or go across in the *Sea Mist*.'

'Well?' He came up the steps of the verandah, studying Susan with cool, calculating eyes. 'Which is it to be? You decide, little one.'

'How could she?' Felicia frowned her disapproval, the excitement in her face fading.

'I agree.' Susan was aware of the tension all around her.

'You must have some idea which you'd enjoy more. By air or sea?'

'Sea!' she said instantly. 'I love water. Particularly the beautiful blue ocean.'

'How priceless!' Felicia gave a tight smile. 'We could get there much quicker in the Baron.'

'That's all right' Devin said lazily, 'I too fancy taking the *Sea Mist*.'

'What the hell if I'm seasick!' Felicia gave him a wry smile. 'We don't know yet what the weather will be like.'

'Then we'll just have to wait and see,' Devin said patiently.

Inside the hallway, Trish Conrad called to them, the light from the chandelier turning her light brown hair to gold. They went forward to join her, but not before Susan caught the expression in Felicia's eyes. It said plainly:

Damn you.

CHAPTER FOUR

IT was from Jess Hansen that Susan learnt the history of the Chandler family. Over numerous cups of tea Jess wove a fascinating history of one of the greatest cattle runs of the Far North. Every Chandler in turn, from John Fitzroy Chandler right down to Devin Chandler, his great-grandson, had had to do battle with an endless set of problems. For 'Fitz' it had been savage natives, white outlaws, tremendous distances and the enormous challenge of carving himself a great holding out of a wild, hostile land. Even today with the countryside transformed, the halcyon climate of the Dry turned savage as cyclones swept in from the Coral Sea and usually brought with them widespread devastation, extensive flooding and loss of life.

Lara homestead had never been evacuated, but it had often been encircled with floodwaters. This scarcely seemed to matter, or the hardships, for each generation had adapted itself more completely to its tropical environment. Lara was entirely self-sufficient, an independent kingdom, with the resources and the ability to help isolated communities in trouble. The airstrip was all-weather, the homestead when battened down a formidable fortress, lending a sense of security to those fortunate to own it. It was impossible for a Chandler to escape power or the responsibility that came with it.

Devin Chandler held the position of protector in this part of the world, both to his own people and the

aborigines on his land. Much was expected of him and
he had been subjected to a harsh discipline right from
his earliest years. Though it was said his father cared
for him more deeply than any other living creature, he
very rarely showed it, understanding only that his elder
son had to be trained for his future position—the
custodian of Lara. Such a position was sacred and
Devin Chandler had been instructed in a hard school, a
school that would have broken his brother and that
drove Nadia Chandler to remove him from his father.
As Jess put it, some were born to take their natural
place, but it took steel.

'Did Emma's father look like Devin?' Susan leaned
back in her chair and stared at the calendar behind
Jess's head.

'A family likeness, no more. The truth is, dear, there
was more of the likeness between Mr Devin and his
mother. She was a very striking-looking woman, and
she had those green eyes. Gave up everything when she
left him behind. Of course Mr Chandler would never
have let him go—his son and heir, and above and beyond that he idolised the boy. A very complicated
man was Mr Chandler, but we were all devoted to him.
Even as a boy Mr Devin showed great character. But
oh, wasn't too much weight put on his shoulders! His
father spoke to him and treated him like a man. That
kind of thing, when he was only a boy. Such a handsome boy, and so full of character. He always looked
after his brother, jumping in to protect him from their
father. It was too much to expect Mr Chandler would
have two sons of equal calibre. Mr Bradley was vulnerable in a way his brother wasn't or, at least knew
how to hide. Even as a lad he had to ride and shoot and

cut cattle as well as men who had been doing it all their lives. Mr Chandler used to take him into rough country and leave him there. It would have been the end of young Bradley, but Mr Devin always found his way back to the homestead.'

'How extraordinary!' Susan dropped her eyes to the housekeeper's tanned, homely face. 'I begin to see why his mother suffered.'

'Mr Chandler wouldn't brook interference. The great mercy was that Mr Devin was the eldest son. Not that Mr Bradley wasn't a highly capable man : he was. It's just that he would never have grown into his father's shoes. We were all deeply shocked when he was killed.'

'I can imagine!' Susan said. 'Poor little Emma!'

'You've done wonders with the child,' Jess Hansen nodded her head emphatically. 'I just don't have the knack, yet I try and try. Poor little soul! Before you came it used to be heartbreaking watching her creep into corners and stay there.'

'Whom does she resemble?' Susan looked up curiously.

'I don't blame you for asking,' Jess's mouth went wry. 'They're all such a handsome bunch! I'm sure our little Emma will improve in time, but I can't think of anyone exactly. Mrs Chandler has dark eyes and there was a time she had dark hair. It reached right down her back. There was a time there. . . .' For a moment it looked as if Jess was about to go on, then she obviously reconsidered, pushing another delicious little cake in Susan's direction. Telling the family history was one thing, but gossiping about them was another.'

*

During their afternoon swim, with the sunlight dropping through the branches on to Susan's young slender body, she looked up to see Rick Gardiner stepping carefully down the bank so as not to disturb her. Instantly she swung up into a sitting position, adjusting the straps of her bikini top. Her halter-necked wrap was somewhere behind her along with Emma's flowered sundress.

'Hi!' There was something in the light blue eyes, some expression, that disturbed her.

'Oh, hello!' Embarrassed, she pushed her dark red curls into some semblance of order. She just knew they were flaming around her face.

He knelt beside her, his voice so low it didn't reach the child in the water. 'You *are* beautiful!'

'I can't seem to get a tan.'

'Why would you want to?' he asked softly, his eyes on her incredibly silky skin. 'I've been wanting to meet up with you for days.'

'Oh?' Her blue eyes were tinged with purple.

'You're not afraid of me, are you?'

'God heavens, no!' Not afraid, she thought, but wary. She was woman enough to read desire.

'Shy little thing, aren't you? You remind me of a flower.'

'I wasn't expecting anyone,' she returned a little bluntly.

'Hey, wait now,' he laid his fingers against her wrist, 'the last thing I want to do is offend you.'

'I've never been any good at small talk, and excessive compliments only embarrass me,' she shrugged.

'Then you're different from every other girl I've met!' He smiled suddenly and his white teeth were dazzling. 'I'm going to have a talk to you while I can. There's no sense in being ashamed of being beautiful. We don't meet all that many beautiful girls up here.'

'How long have you got left on Lara?' Susan asked the question merely to change the subject. Emma was well aware that they had company, but she was staying in the shallows until Rick had left.

'Another few months.' The blue eyes were very bold, making her more ill at ease. 'Dad was friends with Dev's father for a whole lot of years. On Lara I'm very much one of the juniors, but when I get home I'll be boss. My dad had a heart attack a couple of years ago and now we just want him to relax.'

'I can understand that. But why did you come here?'

'You know nothing about the business, to ask that,' he said easily. 'Lara's a legend. There's nothing I can't learn here—more in a week than I'd have to contend with in a year back home. Dad figured I couldn't afford to miss out on the experience. He put it to Dev and he agreed. He knew how important it was to the old man. If a man can run a place the size of this, he can run anything.'

'It is rather awesome,' she said thoughtfully. 'Surely you should be doing something around the property now?'

Rick smiled at her crookedly. 'Are you trying to get rid of me?'

She shook her head. 'I was just thinking Emma wouldn't come out of the water until you left.'

'A funny little thing, I'll grant.' His glance towards the splashing child was expressionless. 'A number of people are wondering just who she is.'

'I beg your pardon?' She turned her face to him, astonished.

'You don't care, do you? It's got nothing to do with you.'

'I don't even know what you mean.' Her eyes were fixed on his face without really seeing him.

'When they married, Brad and dear Felicia, she was hopelessly in love with Dev."

'You've no right to say that!' she protested, dismayed.

'Honey, it might be a little too much for you, but half the State knew it. Somebody has to tell you. You'll sure as hell hear it some time. Brad was a nice bloke, I liked him, but dear Felicia did him no good.'

'Please, this is none of my business.' She tried to get up, but his strong hand held her easily.

'Don't get sore. Honesty is always the best policy. However beautiful she was then, Felicia didn't tempt Dev into marriage. Maybe no woman will, except for one problem. Who's going to be the next keeper of the flame? There are cousins, shareholders, city folk who come thousands of miles to speak to Dev, but a man wants a son of his own. If Dev said no to Felicia once, he'll say it again.'

'Then you'll just have to wait and see,' she said in a careful, low voice. 'It distresses me to ask you, but what did you mean about Emma?'

He raised his hand and flicked away an iridescent insect. 'You want to get your eyes open. I mean, who does the kid look like? Felicia, though she's a ruthless bitch, is pretty damned beautiful. The brothers, Dev and Brad, *their* father and mother and grandparents were really good-looking people by anyone's standards.

Maybe you want to be kind to the kid, but you must have noticed she's terribly plain.'

'By the same token, I hope you're aware that children change,' she said sharply. 'I hope you're not implying that Mrs Chandler lost her head with someone outside the family.'

'Indeed I am!' he answered with great conviction. 'Argue as you will, the kid's looks don't match up with anyone. Not the splendid Dev's, not poor old Brad's, nor the various members of Felicia's family. Interesting, is it not?'

'And it means precisely nothing,' Susan said firmly. 'God knows Emma was devoted to her father. Do you think the child wouldn't know her own?'

'I really wouldn't know.' He collapsed on the bank beside her. 'Like I told you, Brad was a really nice bloke. Both of them had a hell of a childhood, separated and all the rest of it, but Brad worshipped the ground his brother trod upon. To give Dev his due, he does rather inspire devotion. He was always the biggest, the strongest, the bravest, the eldest, but there was no competition between them. Not even over Felicia. She baited a trap all right, but she got the wrong brother. That's the heart of it, Susan. Brad was a big enough fish, but it didn't take his wife long to look in a few other directions.'

'Please stop!' Susan rose swiftly to her feet. 'I think it's a pretty contemptible story. And if you looked a lot closer you'd see the child has potential. Plenty of thin little waifs have grown into amazingly beautiful women. It's my belief she looks like her mother.' Her wide eyes were dark blue, a brilliant shock of colour in her small, flushed face. She stood perfectly still above him, for once unaware of how she looked to him in the brief navy blue bikini.

'I bet you were a beautiful baby!' he said softly. 'All the way!' Very slowly he raised himself to his full height beside her. 'Would you come riding with me if I asked you?'

'I don't really have the time.'

'You're too sensitive.' He glanced at her a little impatiently. 'Why in the world should you let a bit of gossip upset you?'

'Gossip can be damning,' she said huskily. 'I wouldn't do it myself.'

'Then I'm sorry. I apologise sincerely. I guess I was only trying to make conversation. On top of that, I just want to show you some places that will interest you. You've been pretty much tied up with the child, I know, but you deserve a break.'

He sounded so serious and sincere, Susan sighed. 'I'm sorry too, but the truth is I'm only here for a short time.'

'What was my mistake?' His curving mouth went hard.

She didn't answer but moved back a little to pick up the brilliantly patterned sarong.

'Susan?' Emma was hesitating, looking up at them, but she had come out of the water.

'Hello there!' Rick gave the little girl a charming smile.

'Hello,' she replied, then said firmly, 'Shouldn't you be at work for Uncle Dev?'

It was so composed yet so spirited, Susan could have cheered out loud, particularly when Rick started and gave the child a bright, long glance. 'Yes, of course, you're right, Miss Chandler. I'm supposed to be on duty, but I'm glad I came down all the same.' Instantly he transferred his glance to Susan, absorbing skin, slender limbs and curves, her bright colouring. 'I have a half a day, Thursday. There's a lot I could show you.'

'I'll let you know,' Susan said, as much to get rid of him as anything else.

'So I'll content myself with that.' He saluted her, took a few steps up the bank, then stood still as he realised a horse and rider were closing in on him at every stride.

'Who sent you down here?' Devin Chandler rode into sight, a striking figure on a beautiful big black gelding. His voice rang authoritatively, registering his disapproval.

'Sorry, Mr Chandler,' Rick tried to laugh. He waved one hand behind him a little vaguely. 'I just saw the girls, so I decided to say hello.'

The older man nodded, looking irritated and intimidating. 'You have a job to do, not to mention getting paid a good wage. Move off.'

'Yes, sir.' Rick lengthened his stride until he was quickly out of sight.

It seemed to Susan Devin would see her heart hammering. He dismounted, looped the reins around a branch and came down the bank, his dark face taut, glittering eyes like gems.

'How much time did he spend here?'

His voice lashed out at her so suddenly, Susan very nearly recoiled. 'I don't know. T-ten, fifteen minutes.'

'Damn it all, you should have sent him away.'

'I did!' Emma spoke up unexpectedly.

'Good girl!' Devin Chandler ran his hand quickly over the child's damp head. 'I expect you to take care of our guest.'

'I think he upset her,' Emma added, worldly-wise.

'Did he?' Devin Chandler's green eyes moved deliberately to Susan's face.

'Oh, no!' She scarcely knew what else to say. 'I'm surprised you thought that, Emma.'

'You were pleased to see me all the same,' Emma observed with another flash of adult understanding.

'It might be an idea to put up a Keep off the Grass sign,' her uncle remarked with hard mockery. 'At the very least, Susan, you could have put on your wrap or whatever it is you're clutching so modestly.' His eyes travelled the length of her slender frame.

'I didn't expect to see anyone,' she said pointedly, unexpectedly shaking with temper.

'No?' His laugh was brief and unamused. 'Don't worry, you won't be bothered again.'

With her cheeks flushed and her eyes sparkling she drew the sarong around her and tied it around her neck in a halter.

'Susan's been giving me swimming lessons,' Emma offered, instinctively trying to help her friend.

'Has she now?' Devin Chandler looked at his niece suddenly. 'No wonder you've been looking so superbly fit. What about showing me?'

The little girl's face went bright with colour. 'Not now.'

'Why not?' Susan flashed her an encouraging glance, rather surprised at so much conversation from the usually quiet child. 'You're quite good for your age.'

'Oh. Yes, I suppose so. All right then.' Dark eyes

softened, but in a very businesslike manner Emma waded into the lagoon, turned and waved, then struck out more vigorously than she had ever attempted before.

'You're a good kid!' Devin Chandler turned to look down at Susan, standing so gracefully by his side.

'And you're a beast!' Immediately she said it she gave a despairing little sigh. How ridiculous she always made herself!

'Because I told your boy-friend to take off?' his eyes were gleaming and a smile played around his chiselled mouth.

'I'm not interested in boy-friends.'

'I'm glad you told me,' he said dryly. 'I won't stand for any fraternising with the staff.'

'I gathered *that* from your tone,' she answered recklessly. 'If I disobey do you whip me?'

'I think I could think of something better than that.' He wasn't looking at her, but straight ahead at Emma, who had taken to floating gently on her back.

She looked up at his dark profile, not quite understanding, but at least he no longer looked angry.

'Do you think I could ride some time?'

'I'm sorry!' he turned back to stare at her. 'Of course you can. You look so damned fragile it's just incredible to think you can.'

'I can!' she smiled faintly and waved at Emma, who was about to give an exhibition of back-stroke.

'How well? Be certain I'm going to check you out.'

'Really? Whatever for?'

'Do you find that surprising?' he asked dryly. 'It's very important I know you can handle yourself properly, let alone one of my horses.'

'So it's the horse you're fussy about?' Susan was feeling a little lightheaded, hearing herself just talking to him.

'I don't know that I am, and I love my horses.'

She looked at him, trying to see if he was serious and when his green eyes met hers briefly she began to panic. He made her come alive in the most terrible way. She could do no more than stare at him, wanting to reach out and just touch him. He was very tall, his shoulders beneath the bush shirt very wide. Everything about him moved her unbearably. It was dangerous and stupid and it should make her angry. This man came from a different world and soon all of it would be ended. Over. Done with.

'What is it about me that makes you so nervous?' he asked her, just above his breath.

'I can't handle station owners all that well.'

He smiled. 'Just think of you with kids! I think that's about it with Emma. She's tiring herself out.'

'Call her, she'll come to you.'

'Right!' He smiled at her before he moved down to the water and the molten sensation it created inside her made her sink her teeth in her soft, moulded underlip.

It made her feel disloyal just to think of what Rick had told her. Had Devin Chandler been Felicia's real love? Doubts were so easily spread, and certainly she was fascinated by him now. More disturbing was the charge about Emma. It had been totally unnecessary for Rick to have mentioned it. The scandalmongers could agree all they liked, the child resembled no one, but a man like Devin Chandler could not possibly be fooled. He treated Emma as his niece, his late brother's only child, and for a few seconds when she had spoken up to Rick Gardiner, she had been every inch a Chandler.

How cruel it would be for the child to hear any such talk! She had witnessed enough conflicts between her mother and father. Now she was coming out of the water, water glistening all over her thin little body, unwilling to take her uncle's hand, but walking quietly beside him looking up at him as if, despite herself, he still had the same old attraction.

'That was very good, Emma.' Susan went forward smilingly, holding out Emma's towel.

'Another plus for Sweet Sue!' Devin Chandler commented over the child's head. 'Show me you can ride and I'll give you my best horse.'

True to his word, Devin Chandler got down to the business of checking out her riding ability the very next morning. Though she wasn't an accomplished rider, mostly from lack of practice, she had a natural seat and good hands, and most of all she loved horses.

'Good girl, all you need is riding time.' He watched her dismount, then passed the reins to a stock boy who walked her mare off.

'I didn't think I'd passed the test, with all that criticism.'

'Constructive, my child.' He glanced into her warmly tinted face. 'You're a long way from being expert yet.'

'I haven't ridden for ages,' she explained.

'So you want a good quiet horse. The mare will do very well.'

'But she's beautiful!' Susan exclaimed.

'I'm glad you like her. I can relax knowing you're on her.' Sunlight struck blue off his very black hair. 'Take her out every day, but don't ride alone any distance from the house.'

'I promise,' she said sweetly, and he twisted a lock of her hair, forcing her to look up at him.

'You'd better do what I say.'

'Of course!' Her eyes clung to him.

'All right then!' From sounding grim, he smiled. 'I have a bit of time, do you want to look around the complex?'

'I'd love to!'

She was a complete stranger to the world of a great cattle station and it was wonderful just to walk around with him. An education.

From the stable complex they walked deep into a green paddock where about forty good horses were grazing.

'I've always loved horses,' she told him. 'It must be heaven to have them around all the time.'

'You surprise me!' He slanted a glance at her flushed, entranced face. 'If you want to know the hard truth, I've been thinking of you as a hothouse flower.'

'Definitely *not*!' She laughed—she had to. 'Anyway, don't the blue lotus grow wild in the lagoons?'

'Let me see, who's been talking?'

'You *did* call me that?' The breeze skeined her thick silky hair around her face and her neck.

'God knows it's the colour of your eyes,' he replied.

When Susan returned to the house by a side path she heard the murmur of voices up on the verandah. One was Felicia's somewhat drawling accent, the other Jeff's. Surprise kept her quite still, so she was able to catch the seductive note in Felicia's seemingly casual enquiry. It must be boring for her lounging around the homestead all day. She was not at all an outdoors person, and Jeff couldn't hide his faintly hostile attraction.

Protectively Susan almost ran to reach her brother, calling out gaily, 'Why hello, Jeff!'

'Hi!' He swung about to face her, young-man lean, and very attractive.

Felicia was reclining in one of the planter's chairs, looking beautiful and dramatic even at that hour of the morning. 'Your brother has won for himself an afternoon off,' she explained languidly. 'I believe he's planning on a little outing for you both.'

'Any time you say, Jeff.' Susan reached out swiftly and touched her brother's hand. 'Devin's let me have one of the mares.'

'Really?' Felicia flashed her a straight look. 'So that's where you went. God knows what'll come of it.'

Jeff stared at her, his eyes narrowing. 'We'll manage.'

'Okay, okay!' Felicia gave a little relaxed laugh and slumped further into the chair. 'You're both very touchy, really, wouldn't you say?'

Jeff considered her for a minute, then turned away to speak to his sister. 'If you won't find it too tiring I thought we'd ride out to the gorge. Or perhaps we could take the Land Rover. You decide.'

'What's out there?' Susan asked.

'Magnificent scenery, if you like that sort of thing!' Felicia drawled. 'Cave drawings. Visitor's aren't allowed to come on to the property to view them without permission from Dev. He's determined to protect them for future generations and so forth.'

'We need someone like that,' Jeff answered a trifle shortly. 'The North has some of the richest galleries in the continent. Probably there are hundreds of important sites no white man has ever seen.'

'So they claim,' Felicia yawned delicately. 'If you're going out there, probably I should see them myself.'

Susan couldn't believe it. Surely Felicia didn't intend to come with them?'

Jeff's high-cheekboned face had an unaccustomed flush. 'You're very welcome. In which case, we'll need proper transportation.'

Felicia laughed huskily. 'I'm glad you don't expect *me* to ride.'

'Perhaps you'll allow Emma to join us?' Susan enquired, feeling her whole afternoon had been ruined.

'Why not?' Felicia waved a languid hand. 'Though you'd better know at once, you'll have to look after her.'

I'll bet! Susan could see the picture. She and Emma and a bored seductress fascinating her willing-to-be-fascinated brother. Jeff's hard blue gaze was visibly caressing Felicia's matt white skin. Finally he found his voice.

'Well then, I'll see you this afternoon.' He settled his cream Stetson at a rakish angle and nodded briefly at his sister.

'Fine.' Felicia watched him through narrowed eyes. 'Say twoish. Dev will be in for lunch.'

In the distance dust rose in a pink cloud over the horse yards. Even in the moving vehicle they could hear the shouts of the stockmen and the maddened squealing of the horses.

'What's going on?' Susan asked from the back.

'They're herding the brumbies,' Jeff said. 'One of the boys is doing some breaking in. They reckon there's not a horse alive that won't respond to him.'

'It must be terrible for them to lose their freedom,' Emma said quietly to Susan.

'Speak up, dear.' Felicia barely turned her ash-blonde head. 'It's not polite to whisper.'

Emma moved closer to Susan, but she passed no more remarks.

'Would you like to drive past?' Jeff asked no one in particular.

'You're joking!' Felicia looked down at her cream silk shirt. 'It's utterly cruel. Man's business, and we'd get covered in dust.'

'You don't ride?' Jeff glanced at her very briefly.

'What gave you that idea?' It was hard to tell the expression in her dark eyes behind the Christian Dior sunglasses. 'I used to ride a great deal. One has to in this kind of country, but I haven't really a strong love of horses. Motor cars suit me better.'

'What are your other accomplishments?' Jeff asked. There was some note in his voice Susan didn't recognise, but apparently Felicia did.

She gave a hiccough of genuine laughter. 'Perhaps I'll find the time to tell you.'

In the back seat, Emma pressed Susan's hand, a look in her brown eyes Susan found both unchildlike and disconcerting. Emma's intuition was as strong as a woman's and she knew her mother was being deliberately provocative. Probably, Susan thought sadly, from experience. Nervous herself, she clasped the child's hand in her own, surprised to find it cool and clammy when the mirage shimmered all around them.

The homestead and the outbuildings and bungalows

that surrounded it like satellites were long lost to view. Away to the left two black stockmen on horseback waved to them and Jeff honked the horn in acknowledgment. They were out on the open savannah now where a small herd were grazing. Distinctive humps, large drooping ears and dewlaps marked the beasts as Brahmans, a breed sacred to the Hindus, and imported into Northern Australian cattle stations where they withstood heat and tropical disease.

The sky overhead was an incredible cobalt, and colonies of birds accompanied them overhead like a pageant; so beautiful, so brilliantly coloured, Susan could hardly take her eyes off them. In the front of the vehicle Jeff and Felicia continued to hold a murmured conversation as though unaware they weren't alone and to distract Emma's avid attention, Susan began a conversation of their own. The scenery was so beautiful; absolutely remarkable because of the vast distances, the lush grasses that swept the sides of the vehicle, and the hectically blossoming trees, she should have been enjoying herself immensely. Instead she felt sick with apprehension. Felicia was too smooth for Jeff. Too unscrupulous. But whatever Susan thought, neither Jeff nor Felicia noticed her. Or Emma.

The fresh new leaves of the trees were a brilliant red in colour and they skirted a deep lagoon where swamp plants grew and flowered profusely. The open tea tree forests were turned to swamps in the wet season, but the first of the storms hadn't yet begun. The wet season was violent through December to March and Susan had a vivid mental image of the whole area when subjected to torrential, cyclonic rain.

From the still, shining surface of the swamp, thousands of wild geese rose in a cloud, disturbed by the roar of the engine. 'What an extraordinary sight!' Susan said delightedly.

'You're a real little nature girl, aren't you?' Felicia scoffed.

'So am I,' Emma piped up, but quietly. 'You should see the brolgas dance their courtship rituals, Susan. It's absolutely marvellous, they're so graceful and they really do do ballet steps. The jabirus like to flirt as well. You can always see them around the lagoons.'

'I'll have to slow down,' Jeff told them. 'In fact the going will be a lot easier on foot to the escarpment. It's honeycombed with caves and fissures and gorges.'

'I love it more than anywhere on Lara,' Emma told Susan softly. 'The whole cliff face looks like a big sailing ship.'

'Then you've seen it before?' Susan looked down into the child's softened face.

'Yes, with Daddy and Uncle Dev.'

Increasingly the child was coming to mentioning her father and Susan looked at her with affection and approval. 'Often?'

'No, just the once.' Emma spoke wistfully, almost abstractedly, her dark eyes on the back of her mother's elegant head. Emma was suffering from a dreadful feeling of insecurity and her mother's egocentric nature wasn't helping.

Under the fragrant wild quinine trees Jeff brought the Land Rover to a halt. 'Once the rains start we'll never get in here,' he told them.

Felicia remained seated in the vehicle obviously waiting for Jeff to assist her, but Susan and Emma quickly scrambled out, gazing all around them. 'The sound of silence!' Susan held up her slender arm like a dryad. 'Surely this is another world!'

'In my grandfather's time absolutely no one came here but us. Us Chandlers.' Emma's grave little voice held a ring of pride. 'This was, and still is, sacred ground. But can't you just tell benevolent spirits guard it?'

'Yes, I can!' Out of the side of her eyes, Susan could see Felicia hadn't broken free of Jeff's supporting arm. 'It does look like a magnificent galleon in full sail. How odd!'

'It's been here, probably millions of years.'

Susan nodded and took the child's hand. 'Coming, Jeff. Mrs Chandler?'

'The going is easy around the foot,' Jeff called to her. 'There's nothing to be afraid of.'

'We're not!' Emma whispered quietly up to Susan. 'Come on, I'll show you. If you see a flash in the bush, it might be a dingo, but don't worry, it'll quickly slink off.'

'I hope so!' Susuan was incensed and upset that Jeff preferred to make the climb with Felicia.

'Take care,' Emma warned her, jerking on her hand. 'It can be a bit tricky, you know.'

'Sorry,' Susan apologised swiftly. In her high, sarcastic, superior manner, Felicia seemed intent on demonstrating she could fascinate any man she pleased. Jeff should know that, of course, which meant he deserved what he got, but Susan had a great regard for her brother's happiness. They had always been so close.

Gulping down her anxieties, Susan managed to keep up Emma's pace. The child was as agile-footed as a mountain goat and now she was filled with the joy of showing Susan whole walls of caves covered with people and strange beings; crocodiles and great snakes; dingoes and kangaroos and all the animals and creatures of the rain forest.

'It's so beautiful here. So different.' They had reached the cool mouth of a cave and Susan and Emma stood still waiting for the others to join them.

Felicia wore her maddening smile, and the brightness of Jeff's eyes betrayed his violent attraction. 'There, that didn't take long!' Jeff scarcely looked at his sister, but he closed his hand encouragingly over Emma's shoulder. 'You didn't tell me you were such a fast mover.'

'No,' Emma said firmly.

'Well now, you're a deep one!' A crooked smile round his mouth, Jeff pulled the vegetation away from the mouth of the cave. 'I suppose I'd better go in first just in case there are bats.'

'I'm sure I'd be delighted to let you,' Felicia drawled. Despite the hot climb her rather heavy make-up was perfectly fresh. She smiled graciously at her daughter but made no move to put out her hand. In consequence for the rest of the afternoon Susan and Emma kept very much together.

They went from one cave to another while Susan exclaimed at the variety and complexity of the drawings. These native shelters glowed with colour, executed in ochres, pipeclay and charcoal, red, yellow, white and black. The walls and even the ceilings were covered with beings or stylised designs, hunters dancing and camping; fish, snakes, crocodiles, running brolgas and so on. There was even a honeymoon cave where the drawings were so explicit that after a brief look, Susan drew Emma outside.

'It's all right!' Emma said sedately, suggesting she knew all about it but didn't wish to cause Susan any embarrassment. 'Uncle Dev thinks there are more sites on the property, but he hasn't got the time to go exploring.'

'They're absolutely fascinating!' Heat clung to Susan's temples and her neck ached from staring upwards at the cave roofs.

'Tourists arrange to come out here in groups,' Emma told her. 'That's if Uncle Dev gives his permission. Some of the Beings are very strange, aren't they? They look like visitors from out of space.'

'I'm sure Erich von Daniken would like to see them,' Susan smiled.

'Yes, I know. Chariots of the Gods.' Emma turned her head as Felicia and Jeff sauntered out again into the sunshine.

'Say you've seen enough.' Felicia freed another button on her silk shirt. 'The humidity is increasing.' Her cheekbones were faintly flushed and she seemed suddenly tired, the energy draining out of her.

'We'll go back if you like.' Susan ducked her head as a huge white cockatoo swooped low to screech at them before it lifted in a white drift of feathers and shot away.

'We've hardly seen anything yet,' Emma protested.

'We can come another time,' Susan said lightly, as Felicia's expression changed, and her narrow lips tightened.

'Enjoy it, Sue?' Jeff asked, gazing directly at his sister for the first time.

'I loved every minute of it,' she said truthfully. 'It's a wonderful place.'

'Personally I found it a little tiresome.' Felicia's relaxed mood had definitely passed. 'The heat doesn't suit me.'

Jeff turned back to look at her, his blue eyes shadowed by thought. 'We'd better get back down again, then,' he said with certainty. 'I can always bring the girls another time.'

Felicia didn't reply but dusted an imaginary speck of dust from her beautiful expensive shirt.

'Right, Sue?' Jeff cleared his throat.

'Yes.' She glanced away abruptly, not liking the tension in her brother's face. Intuition told her Felicia might be a cruel woman even in her loving.

Emma with dust on her pink sun-frock had already left them behind and Susan hurried after her, skidding on a pile of loose stones, and stopping herself by grasping at the trunk of a slender gum. 'Wait for me, Emma!'

Emma bunched her narrow shoulders and came to a halt.

Susan reached her and caught hold of her arm. 'Don't be disappointed, dear. I saw such a lot, and we can always come again.'

Emma made no answer and as they completed their descent a jagged piece of rock pitched away from the cliff face above them and struck Susan forcibly in the back near her left shoulder.

Jeff's shout of warning still floated in the air:

'Sue, look out!'

The impact sent her sprawling to her knees, hands out to stop her momentum.

'Oh, Susan!' Emma's stifled little gasp was urgent with concern. 'Did you hurt yourself?'

Jeff landed heavily beside her, twisting his arm around the woody pillar of eucalypt. 'What a rotten thing to happen! Are you all right, Sue?'

'Yes.' She sat back beside him looking down ruefully at her hands. The palms were all grazed and the knuckles of her right hand scraped.

'Is she all right?' Felicia was standing above them, more irritated than concerned.

'Please!' Susan stood up, the fright making her feel near tears. 'I'm O.K.'

'Are you sure?' Jeff put his now grubby hand on her shoulder and she winced.

'Bruised, a little shaken, no more. Come on, Jeff, let's go back to the Land Rover.'

'We've got ointment and liniment at home,' Emma croaked. 'That rock must have been really heavy. I heard the thud.'

'At least it didn't tear your shirt,' Jeff said, studying her back. 'Better take a look at it when we get back.'

'I'm beginning to wonder if you're jinxed,' said Felicia, her brow lightly furrowing.

'Accidents are always happening in this part of the world,' Jeff broke in. The expression of concern on his face was heartwarming and to his credit he stuck to his sister's side all the way back to the Land Rover, leaving Felicia to dodge all the rough bits herself.

'How is it?' Emma asked softly in the moving vehicle.

'I'll stand it!' Susan looked back at the child and smiled. There was a lot more to young Emma than met the eye and her dark brown eyes floating in her thin little face were quite beautiful. It gave Susan a sense of wonder and gratitude to know somehow she was able to offer one lonely little girl friendship and reassurance. Perhaps this was enough to justify her prolonged stay on Lara. And yet there was another reason, wasn't there? One that should make her despise herself. How could she dare to question Jeff's fascination when what she felt for Devin Chandler sent all her senses craving? Lara, it seemed, had been waiting for both of them.

CHAPTER FIVE

SUSAN waited for the house to retire before she made her way to the first aid room. Her shoulder was swollen, stiff and sore and she supposed she could have done with some kind of soothing ointment. As it was, though she had to reveal her hands at dinner she had covered her bruised back with a suitable dress and sat up as straight as she could. Felicia had decided to reveal very little of what happened during the space of the afternoon and beyond saying she had tripped over a tree root, Susan didn't volunteer any information either. Devin Chandler's green eyes had been sharp enough on her. Probably he thought the same as Felicia: she was jinxed.

A faint glow came from under the door of Devin's study, but Susan moved as quietly as a shadow, little girl weary, her small face pale and innocent of make-up, shadowed and hollowed by the increasing pain in her shoulder.

The mirror in the first aid room showed the dazzling contrast between her deeply glowing hair and her white face. She was wearing a dark blue robe over her night-gown and it had the sheen of silk in the brilliant light. Without her slippers on she almost had to stand on tiptoe to look in to it. She looked small and forlorn and she turned away from her own image.

Cupboards lined the walls and when she opened one after the other she hardly recognised any of the contents. Everything seemed to be numbered and she had no idea what was in any of the jars. A lot of it looked like ointment, but it could be anything at all. There were no labels to go by, just this numbering system. Finally she climbed on a chair and began to open the cupboards above her.

'I wondered what the noise was!'

A voice spoke behind her and she swung around appalled, her hand trembling so much a plastic jar spun out of her hand.

He caught it neatly and put it down on a bench. 'You're tired, I can see that,' he said shortly, 'and in pain. I knew it from the way you were holding yourself at dinner. Get down from there before you fall down.' He didn't even let her attempt the small jump but put his hands to her narrow waist and lifted her to the clinically clean tiled floor.

She seemed to sink and he pulled out a chair. 'You hurt yourself, didn't you? I knew you weren't telling me the truth.'

'Don't bully me,' she said faintly.

Abruptly he put out his hand and tilted her chin. 'Don't let's waste any more time. What really happened this afternoon?'

'It was wonderful!' She lifted her blue-violet eyes.

'An agony as well as a pleasure,' he said dryly. 'You must have done more than just fall over.'

'I would have told you, but it didn't seem important.'

'Tell me now,' he invited crisply, a sombre look on his formidable dark face.

'I got hit by a flying rock,' she murmured huskily.

'*Holl!*' He bit out the word.

'Precisely. That's why I didn't tell you. You're perfectly well aware by now that I'm accident-prone.'

'I can't argue with that one!' His green eyes were studying her intently, the pale delicate features, the near fragility of her slender body, roving down the silken robe to her small bare feet. 'Are you going to tell me where it hurts?'

She couldn't look at him fully, feeling so incredibly shy it was actually hurting her to exhale her breath. She couldn't stay here with him at all. She was so very aware of everything about him. She couldn't believe it, but she was so terribly aware of her own body as though she was longing for him to touch it. It was shocking, shocking, and the physical response within her was making it difficult for her to act with any composure at all.

She stood up quickly. 'It's eased already.'

'Susan!' He brought his hand down on her shoulder and instantly the tears stood in her eyes.

'Oh!' she exclaimed.

'It's your shoulder, is that it? Your back?' His voice was harsh and he moved quickly, withdrawing the blue robe from her shoulders.

The colour flamed in her face and she heard his quick intake of breath. 'I've definitely decided to beat you when you're better!' Abruptly he moved away from her and went to one of the cupboards and she tried to pull the robe back up over her nightgown. If it had have been transparent instead of flowered cotton she would have died. As it was she had to bite the inside of her mouth.

'Leave it,' he said, looking hard and impersonal.

Feeling totally defeated, she sank back against the table. 'At least it didn't break the skin.'

'No, but I bet it's giving you hell. May I?' He advanced on her, the words only a formality, because he clearly intended the bad bruising should be attended to. 'Here, hold your hair.' He pushed the thick, silky mass of curls over her shoulder while she bent her tender nape obediently.

Even his touch was professional, gentle but purposeful. She gave only one tentative little shudder as Devin worked the soothing, healing treatment into the bruised skin and the surrounding area of the shoulder blade. 'Is that hurting you?'

Extraordinary as it seemed, she was enjoying it. More. 'No, that's fine.'

'I use it on injuries all the time. But this is my first time on a woman.'

Of course he didn't know the effect of his voice on her. Just an instant's sensuality, turning her so soft and vulnerable.

'I think I'll complete the treatment with a small nip of brandy. It should help make you sleep.' He applied a protective layer of gauze over the ointment and taped it. 'You can stop trembling now.' Gently he helped her back into her robe, not appearing to notice her delicate bare bone structure or the exquisite shape of her breasts.

'Thank you.' She kept her head inclined so he couldn't see into her eyes.

'Said like a very nice little girl. Victorian style.' His expression was mocking, but teasing as well. 'That robe is a lovely colour.'

'Yes—it is nice.' Vaguely she stroked the soft, silky material.

'Dutch courage, that's what you need!' His green eyes looked sardonic and gently he pulled her down into a chair. 'Relax, little one. You were as white as a sheet when I came in, now you're flushed like a rose.'

'It's something about you that does it.' She risked everything and told the truth.

'Do you think I don't know it?' He looked around at her with no surprise on his face.

Susan watched him pour a very small amount of brandy into a glass, add a little water, then walk back towards her, a suffocatingly, disturbing presence. She had never seen a man, let alone met one, who could attract her so violently.

'Drink up,' he invited.

She took a very small swallow, looked at him, then tried another. 'It's ghastly.'

'I didn't expect you to enjoy it. It's for medicinal purposes. You're wound up like a top.'

She could feel the warmth running right down through her, like magic. 'Is that what it is, why people drink?' she asked him.

'You mean you're all warm inside?'

'Yes.' She was all awareness too, though she didn't want to be, the blood drumming in her body.

'Come on, it's time for little girls like you to be safely tucked up in their bed.' He smiled at her and extended his hand, but as she got close to him, how she couldn't tell, her body came to rest exquisitely acquiescent against his lean, powerful frame.

'Susan, are you aware of anything at all?' Gently he grasped a handful of her hair, forcing her to look up at him, her violet eyes huge and a little dazed. 'Susan?' His voice deepened, face tautening, green eyes questioning.

She was too close to him to ever pull away. It was a

dizzying, frightening sensation, the tips of her breasts touching his chest.

'You're not falling in love with me, are you?' He made it sound like the ultimate stupidity.

'No,' she returned very softly, 'I just can't stand up if you're not holding me.'

'Then I'll just have to lift you.'

'No.' A dreamlike sinuousness was overtaking her limbs. She clung to him with her head folded against his chest. 'I know you never believed me, but I *did* dream about you in the forest.'

'Did you dream I made love to you?' His hand descended to slip around her throat, hard fingers tilting her head up.

'No.' She couldn't seem to get her breath and she wanted to cry.

'Why not?' he asked tauntingly, such a stillness about him. 'I find you beautiful. Like this, the most innocent little witch in the world.' His expression had changed and there was a controlled turbulence about him, even a lick of danger.

'Stop talking to me,' she begged frantically. 'My heart's going crazy!' It was insane, but she couldn't help herself, shocked into response.

His hands slid down and tightened about her waist, drawing her to him, and she turned up her mouth in complete surrender, yearning flooding through her. As never before in her life she was longing to be kissed. Crying out to be though she should be ashamed.

There was an unmistakable flash of desire in his brilliant jade-green eyes, then he tormented her no longer, but lowered his head. 'I wasn't going to, Susan, until you tempted me.'

Then his mouth was on hers.... It was a ravishment approaching cruelty and it scared her because she didn't know how to match him. She had no experience, no remembered blaze to draw on. Now the mouth that searched hers was awakening such a hot throbbing within her, such a searing onslaught of emotion, a hungering, she slid her arms up and locked them about his neck.

It was a frantic feeling and she could only go with it, his mouth moving on hers, his strong hands holding her by the hips so he wouldn't hurt her injured shoulder, not that she would have felt the pain. She had never known such shattering pleasure—torture. She wanted him to crush her. Pick her up and crush her. Love her. Hold her. Bind them together—she didn't know.

Heat was emanating from her thin, silky skin, her breathing erratic, her breasts under the blue robe, aching, hurting. She wanted his hands there, thrilling. His mouth. Instinctively she arched her back as though she felt a caress of her naked breast. How quickly she had changed from an undemanding girl to a woman, simply at his hands. A deep arousal.

It was he who broke away, though she couldn't tear her eyes open. He was lifting her, cradling her, quiet darkness around them, the cool night air moving as he carried her through the house and into a room. The softness of a bed rose up to meet her, the dazzle of light near her eyes.

'Susan?' His voice was barely above a murmur.

Dazedly she forced her eyes open, meeting his jewelled gaze. She looked feverish, violet eyes enormous, her hair tumbled about her face. She was lying in her own bed and he was bending over her, smoothing her curling hair back from her temples. Treating her like a child when he had brought her tumultuously to an unfulfilled woman's passion.

'What happened?' She shook her head as if to clear it.

His voice was deep, vibrant with self-mockery. 'Sometimes a man lets go, I'm afraid. You're an incredibly sweet little virgin.'

'How do you know?'

'You *are*.' His fingers reached out and lightly grazed her eyelids. 'Go to sleep. I promise you I've got everything under control.'

'You should never have kissed me,' she whispered dreamily, already settling her head sideways into the cool nest of pillows.

'I didn't intend to. Not like that.' He was twisting her gently, easing her robe off. 'In the morning I'm hoping you won't be sure if it happened or you dreamt it.'

'I'll be sure!' she exclaimed in that same quiet, dreamy voice.

He watched her for a moment longer, the light glancing off his arresting dark face. He was a highly civilised man and she was under his protection. Even in sleep her body was arranged innocently, very chaste and graceful. Devin walked to the bedside table and flicked off the light.

'Sweet dreams, little one!' he murmured, if only to himself.

When she awoke, she had no sense of time or place. Her sleep-drugged eyes travelled slowly over the delicate floral motif of the papered walls around her, the serpentine Victorian sofa, two armchairs, the light patterned rosewood dressing table with the lovely oval mirror and on to the green-shuttered French doors.

Her whole body quivered awake and memory came rushing back. She would never be the same again. She was affected for ever. She sat up and a slanting ray of sunlight lit up her hair and silhouetted her slender body through the thin nightdress. 'Oh, Devin!' she breathed. It wasn't an impossible dream. Last night had really happened.

She got up, showered and dressed, sweetly annihilated by her memories. At different moments she seemed frozen in her actions as she was seized by the same dazzling excitement she had felt last night. She couldn't be mistaken. He would never have kissed her in that way unless she moved him. She couldn't be mistaken, otherwise she would die.

When she finally found her way to the breakfast room, Felicia was already seated at the table, her ash-blonde hair smoothly tied at the nape, a far-away look in her deep, dark eyes.

'Good morning.' Susan went to the sideboard and peered under the covered warming dishes.

Felicia disdained such little courtesies but looked up to study Susan very steadily. 'You're very late.'

'I slept in.' Susan poured herself some pineapple juice, transferred a luscious slice of pawpaw to a bowl and sat down. 'Did you sleep well?'

'With the help of my pills.' Her voice was cool and indifferent.

'Where's Emma?' Susan asked, smothering the vague resentment that was stirring in her. Felicia with her own sex made no attempt to be pleasant.

'How should I know?' Felicia snapped. 'I hardly see my own child.'

'But you do think she's coming out of her absorption, don't you?' Susan put down her spoon.

'She always was a plaintive child.' Felicia's eyes were still fixed on Susan's transparent face, shadowed with remembered radiance. 'If I had to have a child at all, I wanted a son, a wonderful, handsome boy. Instead I was cheated, I got Emma.'

'You ought to thank God!' It was out of Susan before she could stop it. 'Hundreds of thousands of women desperately long for a child of their own and you call it being cheated!'

'I'm sure of it.' Felicia looked at her coldly. 'The deeply maternal type, like you, come a dime a dozen. I belong to a different species.'

'You sound as though you consider that a big mark in your favour!'

'I do.' Felicia glanced at her wrist watch and gave a hard little laugh. 'Surely you know a man wants more of a woman than just being the mother of his children.'

'Some would consider it of infinite importance.'

'Little fool!' Felicia laughed at her. 'What would you know about it anyway? I'll bet you've never been in bed with a man in your life.'

'And I prefer it that way. At least until I'm married.' Delicious as the pawpaw was, Susan couldn't eat it. Felicia didn't exactly make an easy companion.

Now she clicked her tongue contemptuously. 'Keeping yourself, are you, dear? How quaint! Think what joy you'll give to some lucky man. You simply mustn't give in!' Suddenly she was serious, Susan saw it in her dark eyes. 'You wouldn't be having any romantic little notions about Dev, would you? Quite simply, dear, you wouldn't have a chance. Dev doesn't give a damn about how many hearts he breaks. I should know—he broke mine. The one man in my life I've loved and he laughed at me! He's a cruel devil, and I wish I knew how to stop loving him.'

'How extraordinary!' Susan looked back at her bemused. 'You don't have to tell me anything!'

'I think I do,' Felicia said tersely. 'One more thing, I'm afraid I'll have to insist you take yourself off after this weekend. A few days on Sunset you're allowed, since Bob and Trish have asked you, but I don't wish you to come back with us.'

'Surely that's for Mr Chandler to tell me.' Upset and shaken, Susan got up from the table.

'You mean you're going to wait for him to tell you to go away?' Felicia quirked a thin black brow. 'Actually, dear, it's my job, because you see, this time Dev's not going to get away from me. Not ever!' She paused then, her eyes narrowed, her body poised like a snake about to strike. 'Don't run away,' she said with a contemptuous little laugh. 'I'm not blind, dear. Did you think I didn't see through all your ingratiating little ways? Helping poor helpless little Emma when you really wouldn't waste a minute of your time.'

'Don't assume I'm anything like *you*!' Susan felt goaded enough to say it. 'I've a very real affection for Emma. For all children.'

'And Dev has nothing to do with it?' Felicia very nearly snarled. 'A lot smarter, stronger women than you couldn't hold his attention. Ask Trish, she'll tell you. Don't think it's enough to have a nice little figure and baby blue eyes. Hell, at your age I was a raving beauty and I couldn't get him. I didn't realise I was going about it the wrong way. But I'm a lot older and wiser now. So's Dev. All I've got to do is sit tight.'

Susan stared down at her whitened knuckles, grasping the chair. 'I was told you didn't love your husband.'

'Brad was a damned fool! ' Felicia made a sound of infinite contempt. 'A poor imitation of the real thing. As if *he* could make me forget Dev. Or any of the others.'

'Please! ' Susan shook her head and held up her hand. 'It's not any of my business.'

'But don't forget it! ' Felicia warned her with deadly quiet. 'No matter what I have to do, I'm going to get Dev. Getting rid of you is just part of the job.'

Susan moved to the door and glanced back briefly. 'You musn't worry about me.'

'You're not that pretty, darling! ' Felicia said dryly. 'In fact, compared to a lot of the others, you're easy. Just a sweet little fool that thinks herself desirable. Enjoy yourself as Bob's guest, then fly away home. Maybe there, you'll have a future.'

The words rang in Susan's ears all day. Felicia wasn't in the least subtle. She was arrogant and possessive and she well knew how to take what she wanted. Poor little Emma! If Felicia considered she had missed out with her daughter, Emma certainly lacked the right mother.

Later on in the afternoon with Emma taking a nap after a very energetic swimming lesson Susan had the slender little mare, Silky, saddled up for her. Though her cheeks were scarlet with feelings of humiliation and the thought that she had really tumbled herself into

Devin's arms she couldn't allow her wretchedness to take control of her. Devin Chandler had offered her his hospitality and she had taken it. She was really a stranger and a kiss, however much it had meant to her, probably didn't mean a great deal to him. She was certainly naïve to think any of her attractions could make a serious appeal to him. What Felicia had told her was bound to be true. He could have any woman he liked.

She had quite a job finding any of the men. With the price of beef soaring the order had gone out to bring all the unherded cattle in for branding, beasts that had been allowed to roam the wilds of the property during the beef slump. They were being mustered in all kinds of ways—horse, bikes, jeeps and by the station helicopter. There were hundreds of cleanskins roaming the great run, sleek with good living, and the mustering had been going on boisterously for days.

Just as she was deciding she would lose herself she could see a holding yard through the trees, and at least a half a dozen men lolling about in the shade. She was so relieved to see them she could have thrown her hat in the air, but instead she rode sedately towards them.

'Sue!' Jeff, squatting beside Rick Gardiner jumped to his feet, stretching his arms high above his lean body. 'This is fine. I wanted to talk to you anyway.'

The men all looked up at her amiably and Susan smiled and dismounted from the beautifully behaved soft-eyed mare while an aboriginal boy, all smiles, came forward to take the reins and walk the horse off.

'Hi!'

Rick Gardiner was beside her, looking her up and down.

'Hello there, Rick.' Susan tried to sound pleasant but not over-friendly.

'What made you decide to drop by?'

'A pity to waste such a beautiful afternoon.' She took her hat off, letting the breeze stir her hair, not knowing the sun through it was making it glitter and dance.

'You're just in time for a good old cup of billy tea!' Jeff smiled at her. 'I never thought I'd develop a habit, but I have.'

'That sounds heavenly!'

'Good. I'll tell Dusty.' Jeff walked off happily.

'Why did you stand me up on Thursday?' Rick looked at her, his light blue eyes a little hard.

'How do you mean—stand you up? We made no definite plan.'

'I told you I had the whole afternoon off.'

'And I'm sure you enjoyed it.' He was standing so close to her she moved away a little, drawing back into the full shade of a tree. Her blue eyes were brilliant in her warmly tinted face and she looked very small and slight here among the men.

Thirty or more bullocks in prime condition were standing closely packed together inside the holding pen. They had been rounded up and separated and were awaiting branding, all perfect cleanskins. 'It must hurt them, mustn't it, the branding iron?' Susan asked.

'Don't worry about it. They're pretty tough!' Rick lit a cigarette and began to draw on it slowly. 'How come you haven't dragged the kid along?'

'Emma stayed home to have a nap,' Susan forced herself to answer lightly.

'They don't leave you much time to get away from

her,' he said somewhat insolently.

'On the contrary, I'm having a wonderful time.'

'But you won't let me talk to you, will you?' His jaw had set as he threw out the challenge.

'You're talking to me now.'

'I'm not!' He came close to her, his narrow face shadowed. 'One of these days I'll have a property of my own. Not Lara, maybe, but a spread any girl would be proud to queen it over. All I'm asking is a little of your time for the two of us to get to know each other better. I have to say it this way because you'll go out of my life and I'll never see you again.'

'Does it really matter?' She stared up at him, searching his eyes.

'Make no mistake about it. I fell for you on sight.'

'Surely not?'

'You asked me. Maybe I didn't mean to, but that's how it happened.'

The admission silenced her and she almost sighed aloud with relief as Jeff hurried back to her carrying a fragrant steaming mug of fresh tea in either hand. 'Here, Sis. Dusty is bringing some scones over in a minute. He wants to meet you.'

'Lovely!'

'Get yours and join us.' Jeff turned to Rick.

'Sure.' Boldly, deliberately, he looked down at Susan. 'This is the nicest surprise we've had this week.'

'You've made a conquest there,' Jeff said cheerily, after Rick had gone.

'I don't like him. He makes me nervous!' Susan answered sharply.

'What do you mean?' Jeff frowned, his glance on her face. 'He's popular with the men for the most part.'

'Except I'm not a man, I'm a woman. I don't want his interest, Jeff. He doesn't attract me at all.'

'Then I'll tell him right now!' Jeff said belligerently. 'He hasn't been bothering you, has he?'

'No.' Deliberately she steered his anger aside. 'Drink your tea, it'll go cold.'

Jeff nodded and sipped, his lean face deeply tanned. 'Felicia asked me along on this trip to Sunset, did you know?'

'No, I didn't.' She shuddered with repugnance at the very mention of Felicia's name. 'Don't go, Jeff. She's playing some little game with you.'

'Do you think I haven't seen that?' he answered tersely. 'I have mixed feelings about Mrs Felicia Chandler. I haven't worked them out yet.'

'Don't even try,' she begged him.

'Equally important, don't *you* go getting involved with the boss. If I'm any judge you're just his type.'

'Maybe we're both being exploited,' she said quietly. 'Why don't we just go home?'

Rick was approaching, so there was no time to say more. Dusty, the camp cook, followed him carrying a plate of scones and remained to share them placidly talking about the hapless things that had happened to him on round-ups.

For ten more minutes the men rested, then as they were deciding on what to do next, Devin Chandler and Harry Tindall, his overseer, rode into camp. Lancing green eyes rested on Susan planted so delicately in among the men, then he dismounted and came her way, his dark face shadowed beneath the pearl grey brim of his hat.

'Where did you spring from?'

His tone was so businesslike it stilled her racing pulses. 'I was riding this way and I saw the men,' she explained. 'I couldn't refuse a cup of tea.'

'Neither can I. Get it for me, Jeff, will you?' Devin glanced sideways at the attentive young man.

'Sure!' Jeff answered obligingly, and moved off.

'You didn't expect to see Gardiner, of course.'

'Maybe I did.' Why, then, had she said that? Unless she was hurt and suspicious. The jubilance of her waking moment was quite gone. She had simply appeased a moment's hunger. Devin Chandler would no more be dominated by a woman than man could dominate nature. 'Mrs Chandler was saying the trip to Sunset is scheduled for this weekend?'

'Yes,' he glanced at her. 'Don't make it sound a real drag.'

'It wasn't supposed to sound like that,' she protested. 'I'd like to go very much.'

'But you're not sure about the company,' he said a little curtly.

'I'm sorry....' her words came out jerkily. 'You're all being so good to me.'

'And you're not going to let me forget it.'

'You're angry.' She turned her head up to look at him, a tall inexorable figure. 'I don't want you to be.'

'You mean only a woman is allowed fluctuating moods? I don't change, little one. I know what I am and I know what I want. And I've got eyes. I know what will happen if you give Gardiner the least encouragement. I'll finish up having to throw him off the property, and that will upset his father, a man I respect and admire.'

Susan closed her eyes for a moment trying to marshall all her will power. 'After I see the island I'd like to go on home.'

'That isn't what you want,' he picked her up tersely, his green eyes ablaze.

'You're not going to make it easy, are you?'

'You're running away. Why?'

'If I stay here, I'll only get hurt.'

Jeff's approach cut off his answer if he had one. He extended his arm and Jeff put the mug into his hand.

'Milk, two sugars?'

'That's fine.' He nodded agreement. 'Stay for a moment, Jeff,' he ordered as Jeff flashed a smile at his sister and went to return to work. 'Harry's made it clear to me you're working extremely well. In fact he's full of praise for your various talents.'

'He never spoke a word to me about it,' Jeff grinned.

'That didn't stop him from talking to me,' Devin Chandler returned the smile. 'You're not afraid to work and you seem to have a sure instinct with horses and cattle. How do you think you'd go managing the out-station?'

Startled and gratified, Jeff studied the older man's face. 'How many men would I have?'

'Four, no more, and one of our best trackers. You'd have to work furiously to bring in the cattle that have been left roaming for the last couple of years, but your wages will be far more attractive and you'll be training for management. If not on Lara, then somewhere else I could place you depending on how you handled the job. If you don't want it, or you don't like the idea of the isolation, just say so.'

'But that would be great!' Jeff's blue eyes were sparkling, but his sister moaned.

'Oh, no, Jeff! Come home.'

'What's there for me?' Gently he put out his hand and traced the curve of her cheek. 'Listen to me, Sue. This life up here suits me. I identified immediately. In a way, I found my direction. If I work hard enough, maybe in time I could finish up with a property of my own. I don't need an empire, just a little spread I could work and call my own. Besides, like some of the boys, I'm prepared to really study the business. Harry talks to me all the time because he knows I'm interested and I catch on quick. I like being a cattleman. It suits me right down to the ground.'

'Well then, I might never see you again.' Susan's hands trembled as she re-set her wide-brimmed hat on her curly head.

'Hey, cut it out!' Jeff looked disturbed. 'Of course you'll see me.'

'Not for long periods of time.'

'I've got to try, Sue.' Jeff's blue eyes were begging her to understand.

'I know, I know....' She tried to smile, but she couldn't.

'I'll ride back with you,' said Devin , his eyes on her averted profile.

'Don't worry.'

'Let's go!' he returned crisply, and his own eyes darkened, reflecting the deep green of the leaves.

'Just one more thing, Mr Chandler,' Jeff spoke up determinedly, 'have you any objection to my going along on this trip to the Reef? I sure would like to go, but I'll leave the decision up to you.'

'Maybe you won't have to go that far,' Devin countered dryly. 'I'm sure your sister would be glad of your company. In which case it's O.K. with me.'

'Thanks.' Jeff's blue eyes gleamed and he turned away quickly to rejoin the men.

Devin Chandler gestured to a stock boy to bring up the horses and in silence he and Susan rode out of camp, little cross-currents of hostility radiating between them. Last night and this morning Susan had felt almost desperately elated, but now her feelings of self-confidence had dropped to a dangerously low level. Women in love were experts at self-delusion. The strong physical attraction, the radiant sparks of excitement she felt in Devin Chandler's presence had made her too vulnerable. Now she was in full retreat from his hard, masculine authority because he had already hurt her and it would soon be all over.

He seemed no more inclined to talk than she did and when they were within sight of the compound he saluted her briefly and left her. Obviously he was busy, but he didn't think her competent enough to find her own way home. She was beyond reasoning anything, upset and disturbed at the way Jeff was being carried away from her so rapidly. Men were really blessed being so ultra self-sufficient. Susan only knew she would miss her brother dreadfully and all of a sudden life seemed empty. The real, cruel truth of the matter would only hit her later. For now she had to retreat into silence with pride her only defence.

Later on in the afternoon, with a thunderstorm brewing, Susan discovered a guitar pushed casually behind a curtain in one of the spare rooms. She had only come into it to check the windows, but now she stood fingering the strings of the beautiful instrument. It needed tuning, of course, but it was in perfect condition. With a little rush of pleasure she sank into a chair, adjusting the strings, then when she was ready, she began to pluck out a little Spanish melody. The guitar and the flute had been her two instruments at training college and though she was far from being expert in either, she had a flair for the guitar that could have been developed further. She had a sweet, true voice with laughter and sadness in it and an excellent ear, and she crouched over the instrument, her ruby-coloured hair swinging forward almost hiding her face. Softly she sang a folk song, fingers and voice gaining confidence, then when she stopped and looked up she found she had an audience.

Emma stood in the doorway, staring at her, the tears sliding silently down her face.

'Darling,' Susan let the guitar slip to the floor, 'what's wrong?'

Emma shook her head numbly.

'Emma?' Susan was by the child's side, bending shelteringly over her. 'Can't you tell me?'

'It's all right!' Emma found her voice and flashed Susan an agitated, watery smile. 'It used to be Daddy's.'

'The guitar?' Susan winced, feeling she had been idiotically rash and insensitive.

'He used to play it a lot.' Emma went forward quietly and picked up the instrument, stroking the polished wood. 'Mummy wanted to throw it out. She's not at all musical.'

'Are you?' Susan moved a few steps forward and sank into a chair.

'I don't know.' Emma ran her fingers lightly back and forth across the strings. 'Aren't you lucky, being so pretty and everything.'

'How do you know you haven't got a talent your-self?' Susan asked boldly. 'I could teach you some chords if you like.'

'I'd like to hear you better,' Emma said a little sadly, and willingly surrendered up the guitar. 'Play whatever you like. It sounds lovely.'

'Are you sure it won't hurt you?' Susan asked gently.

'No, really,' Emma sat down on the carpet looking up at her, 'I like it. I've always liked it. Daddy was going to teach me when he had the time.'

Swiftly Susan bent her head so Emma wouldn't see the shimmer of tears in her eyes. This time she didn't sing but played the same little Spanish piece that best displayed her technique, then when she saw Emma's dark eyes large and smiling, she swung into some catchy little Neil Diamond songs, her voice sweet and warm and rhythmical. She wanted to please the child, further their relationship, help in whatever way she could.

'You're terrific!' Emma said enthusiastically, and they both laughed.

'Not really, but I'm sure I could help you to play yourself.'

'For goodness' sake, sing me something else!' It was growing darker as the storm clouds gathered, but Emma was quite unaware.

'All right, what's next?' Susan thought for a moment avoiding the sad songs, then looking down at her audience of one strummed a popular folk song she was going to invite Emma to join in.

There was a sound in the hallway, then a shrill, metallic voice that cut jarringly across the sweet vibrancy of Susan's performance. '*Stop that!*'

Susan stood up at once, lifting the guitar strap over her head. 'Mrs Chandler.' She looked behind her, recognising the anger in Felicia's white face. She looked more than angry, a little distraught, and leaping up, Emma took Susan's hand, leaning against her.

'How dare you use my husband's guitar without asking!' Feelings of outrage were driving Felicia, making her advance into the room like a tigress.

'I'm very sorry if I've upset you,' Susan apologised, thinking how bad this was for Emma.

Felicia jerked the guitar out of Susan's slack hand. 'Where did you find this?' She glared down at the instrument as though she was about to smash it to pieces.

'There, behind the curtain,' Susan said stiffly. 'I didn't realise it had belonged to Mr Chandler or that I had to ask permission to play it.'

'Come away, Emma!' Felicia ordered, very loudly.

'If you'll just be calm, Mrs Chandler.' Susan flashed the older woman a pleading look. She hated the way Emma was trembling against her, frightened yet resistent to her mother's ugly mood.

'I said come here, Emma!' Felicia repeated, heedless of anything but her own anger.

'No.' Emma hunched her thin shoulders and buried her face against Susan's arm.

'What are you trying to do, lose me my daughter?' Felicia darted forward and caught the child by the shoulder, wrenching her out of Susan's reluctant grasp. 'It's time you moved on, Miss Blake. You're an unsettling influence in this house.'

'Apparently,' Susan answered, knowing herself defeated. She went to leave the room, upset on Emma's behalf but not knowing what else she could do, when Emma set up a highly vocal protest. She began to rant and rave at her mother in a shrill, hardly articulate manner, the freckles standing out on her small distressed face.

'Stop that! Stop that this *minute*!' Felicia hurled the command, but Emma was pulling away from her, going giddily out of control.

'For God's sake!' Devin Chandler stormed through the doorway, catching Emma by the shoulders and turning her around to face him. 'Why the devil are you screaming?'

'Tell him!' Felicia ordered Susan, then fell into a chair as if she no longer had the strength to stand.

'What goes on here?' Devin still held the weeping child. 'Well, Susan?' He met her nearly purple eyes.

She took a deep breath, though her voice still came out shakily. 'I'm very much afraid I upset Mrs Chandler inadvertently. I found this guitar, you see, and loving the guitar I began to play it.'

'So?' He considered the explanation, looking very hard and remote.

'Ghosts!' Felicia cried, then gave a funny little sob.

'I don't believe in ghosts,' he said, his nostrils flaring very slightly.

'Oh God, darling!' Felicia bent her ash-blonde head into her hands.

'And Emma?' he pressed Susan to finish.

'Emma liked it,' Susan answered quietly.

'Oh.' He picked up the guitar and set it down on the table nearby. Emma was giving harsh little indrawn breaths like spent sobs and he picked her up in his arms while she rested her dark head on his shoulder.

'You're mad at us all, aren't you, baby? Mad at everyone except Susan.'

'Oh, Uncle Dev, it was awful!' Emma jerked her head upright to look at him. 'Promise you won't send Susan away. She's my only friend.'

'No, she isn't!' he flashed back at her firmly. 'I love you just the same as I always did and I'm here. Your mother loves you too. She doesn't want to shout at you or have you shout at her, but both of you in your own way have been hurt. You must learn to understand one another.'

A visible shudder shot through Emma's thin little body. 'If you send Susan away I'll die.'

'You won't!' The uncompromising lines of his face checked the child's hysteria. 'You're a Chandler. You've got it in you to get over all the difficulties in life. You can manage if you want to. The affection you feel for Susan is beautiful, but you don't need her. You have yourself. You can be anything. I used to feel torn apart myself when I was your age and a lot older, but I'm still here. I managed. You start reading the newspapers, learn about other children's lives. You're blessed in so many ways.'

'I know.' Suddenly Emma put her arms around his neck and kissed him. 'I love it when you talk to me.'

'Let's see if we can't talk a whole lot more!' His green eyes looked into the child's. 'You know, Emma, you're a strong one, a real Chandler.'

'Am I?' Emma made a curious little sound.

'Believe it, darling, I'll always tell you the truth.' Gently he lowered her to the ground, but kept hold of her hand. 'Go with Susan now, while I talk to your mother.'

'Dear sweet heaven!' Felicia flung back her head almost theatrically. 'Pity, Dev? You *pity* me. I can't stand it!'

At that moment with his green eyes on her, he didn't look compassionate at all, but strong and ruthless, involved with no one except the child. 'Susan, take Emma, please ... *now*.'

Susan moved obediently, while Felicia's dark eyes flashed out pure hatred, taking the child's hand and drawing her across the room to the door. She knew then the storm was more inside the house than without.

Felicia didn't even join them for dinner and afterwards Susan walked out on to the verandah, resting both hands on a vine-covered pillar and trying to empty her mind of everything except the moon and the wind and the night. The storm had washed the world clean and a night bird was singing in the giant fig tree, a beautiful, unfamiliar song. Even the garden was tranquil under the big tropical moon, a glorious fragrance rising from the gardens.

'What are you pondering on, little one?'

He was behind her almost before she was aware of it, a clipped, decisive voice speaking out of the darkness.

'Nothing.' She cast a swift look at him from over her shoulder. 'Just delighting in the night.'

'Really? I didn't think you were in a cheerful mood. How's the shoulder now?'

'Much better.' She swung around to face him, already aroused, her small head on its slender creamy neck tilted back to meet the brilliant, mocking eyes. 'You're something more than a cattle baron. You're a healer.'

'I thought you were treating me as if I posed a

threat,' he murmured. 'Well, what do you say to that?'

'I think you could teach me a hard lesson,' she answered, her expression intensely serious.

'And you want out?'

'I don't believe myself capable of matching you in any way.'

'Don't look so serious!' He caught at her hand and carried it to his mouth.

'Please!' She wasn't acting sensibly, she knew she wasn't, but she had never known anyone who made her feel so desperately a woman.

'Stop that!' he said dryly. 'I don't attack little girls, even big girls.'

'You wouldn't have to!' she returned wryly. 'I don't know what it is, but you make me feel incredibly foolish.'

'Anything else?' He locked his hands around the white wrought iron balustrade and looked out over the moonlight gardens.

'Many, many things.' She tried to speak lightly.

'Too bad you're not going to tell me.'

'I'm not ever going to forget Lara,' she said, and turned to stand beside him.

'No, you're not.' Devin gave her a brief, assessing glance. 'Your brother seems to want to put down his roots here. Or in this part of the world.'

'Jeff was always restive,' she said, bending her glowing head away from the light.

'And you think this is just a passing phase?'

'You're laughing at me. Don't deny it.' There was a pulse flickering in her throat and she looked very young and tender.

'Then I hope you're going to forgive me,' he answered abruptly. 'Your brother deserves a chance and I'm only too glad to have him here at this time. We'll all have a better appreciation of just what he can do in about six months' time.'

'And I'll be some two thousand miles away.'

'You can't share your brother's life, you know. You'll have a life of your own.'

'You think I'm going on too much?'

'I've noticed you and your brother are very close. It makes me wonder about your childhood. You must have been a very lonely little girl.'

'I would have liked to have arranged it differently,' she acknowledged. 'It's so quiet here, so peaceful.'

'Let's walk a way through the garden.' He turned around to glance down at her, his striking dark face shadowed by thought.

'I. . . .' she began.

'I've no abduction scene in mind,' he said dryly. 'And don't deny what thoughts were occupying your mind.'

'They go with the territory,' she smiled.

'Then be brave.' His green eyes gleamed and he let his gaze travel over her, partly mocking, partly responsive. She could sense it.

The knowledge gave her a little feeling of confidence she didn't have before and when he put out his hand she met it with her own, glancing down at their entwined fingers. His hands were very brown and lean, wrists like steel, her own hand baby-soft and white by comparison.

Overhead a fruit bat flapped, but she was used to them by now. The moonlight patterned the garden with pale gold and silver, and pockets of inky darkness.

Beyond the perimeter of the homestead proper, or the Big House as the staff called it, were the staff bungalows, but only occasionally did they catch the glimmer of lights through the trees.

Tentatively at first Susan began to ask Devin questions about the station, life in the tropics, but as he treated all her questions seriously the conversation became more intimate and involved. He told her something of his own life, about his brother, experiences responsible for the break-up of his parents' marriage, stories about the station which might have seemed to some highly colourful but which she knew were exactly true.

She listened intently, until finally he looked down at her. 'How is it you get me to recount what I haven't told most people?'

'Perhaps it's as they say ... ships that pass in the night.'

'I prefer you to stay.' His mouth curled sardonically.

'But you said yourself I'm not needed.'

'Of course. I said that to Emma. The fact is your effect on her has been remarkable. At least stay with us until she returns to school.'

'It's not possible.'

'Can't you spare the time?'

There was an arrogance in his voice that struck at her physically, and she revealed it in the way she came to an abrupt halt. 'That's not fair! You know I can't stay.'

'Would you feel better if I paid you?' he asked. 'You obviously don't enjoy the prospect of being my guest.'

Her heart gave a great lunge at the rapid descent from companionship to his scarcely veiled antagonism. 'Please hear me out,' she said breathlessly. 'However

much I want to help Emma Mrs Chandler doesn't
particularly care for me. Emma *is* looking to me instead
of her mother and Mrs Chandler very naturally resents
it. She's already shown it, quite clearly.'

'I see.' He looked down into her upturned face, her
eyes pools of darkness, her skin luminously pale. 'I
only want you to help Emma. Leave Felicia to me.'

'Naturally!' She turned away impatiently, unable to
contain a little flicker of jealousy.

'What's that supposed to mean?' His steely grip encircled her wrist as he pulled her back to his side.

'I had heard. . . .' she began.

'*What?*' Even in the silvery darkness she caught the
brilliant flash of his eyes.

'It's none of my business.' She tried to break away
from him, but it was quite impossible.

'As I see it, you've been listening to gossip.'

'I have eyes.' She was goaded into being reckless.

'Damn it, you do. Blue-violet.'

Even as she gasped, and her body trembled in reaction, he turned her fully into his arms, shaping the
back of her neck, grasping a handful of her heavy
silken hair, forcing her head up. 'Get the words out,
Susan. They seem to bother you.'

'No, no! What does it matter to me?'

'I'd say it was hurting you. I think of Felicia as my
sister-in-law, my dead brother's wife.'

'Don't tell me.'

'I'd like to slap you,' he said, in a harsh, clipped
voice. 'Just how *do* you evaluate me as a person?'

'I want to run from you.' She felt herself tremble
and his grip tighten.

'Because you're frightened and you're jealous.'

'*No!*' she moaned, because it was true and she was drowning in his physical magnetism, confused, ashamed, tormented.

His arms were about her and he loomed over her, tall and powerful and master of his own world. 'Whatever you've been thinking, you're quite wrong.'

'I told you, I don't want to know!' Her sharp cry interrupted him.

'But you want to condemn,' he countered harshly. 'Just what am I supposed to be doing now, keeping in practice?'

His shadow fell across her, then he was kissing her mouth, one arm trapping her, the other coming up, fingers moving on her throat, enslaving her will. One desperate effort, then her body untensed of its own accord, became incredibly sweet and yielding, letting him see he had triumphed. She wanted this so much, all other considerations were swept out of her mind.

Somehow his anger was being transformed into a deep, driving hunger; appeased by the way she was clinging to him, or her feverish response. Susan didn't know. She only knew he was exploring her mouth deeply for an endless span of time. It was stunning, yet the most natural thing in the world to be crushed up against him, her mouth inviting this ravishing pressure, her body warm and throbbing yet sending out distress signals as if it wanted so much more. No barriers between them. It was madness to allow him this dark stupendous power even as unconsciously she drove him on with her youth and her beauty. He was the golden god of the rain forest and his strength was enormous.

'You do it deliberately, don't you?' His voice was

deeper, more vibrant than she had ever heard it. 'Just when I decide you're a child that needs protection, you show yourself as a woman, the supreme temptress, promising delights I can only guess at.'

'And you couldn't endure it, could you?' She lifted her head, whispering in the scented dark. 'You like to walk alone, like a tiger.'

'Even a tiger has to take a mate,' he said decisively. 'I have a responsibility I can't deny. I need an heir.'

'Order a wife like you'd order a new aircraft,' she suggested with unaccustomed savage sarcasm.

'To be quite honest, little one, I've already picked her out.'

'Someone you're quite at home with?'

'Of course.' He gave a painful little tug on one of her curls. 'I think you should stay and meet her.'

'*Never!*' She raised her two hands in pathetic protest. 'By the time she comes out, I'll be far away from here.'

'On the contrary, she'll be on the island.'

She heard his suave tone, but his arrogant dark face was now right out of focus. Tears shimmered in her eyes and she took a few defensive steps away from him. 'Things don't hurt you, do they? You're rich and you're powerful and you're worldly and so forth. I'm surprised you wasted one minute of your time on me.'

'Someone had to save your life,' he answered with the utmost detachment. 'Life's a jungle too, Susan. I want to make you tough enough to survive.'

Before he had stopped speaking, she was running, thinking she couldn't rationalise anything—her behaviour or his. On the pathway a big cane toad with a lizard in its mouth frightened her and she cried out hysterically:

'Get out! Oh, get out!'

'What the hell is it now?' Devin had overtaken her easily, lunging out to catch her agitated body.

'A great toad.'

He actually laughed as though he was enjoying himself. 'Let me shift it before it brings on a nervous crisis.'

'You brute!' Helplessly she watched him touch the toe of his shoe to the toad, who took a giant leap away into the dark, the lizard still hanging out on either side of its mouth.

'Come on,' he urged her, amused eyes on her small, moody face. 'Let's go inside and have an aspirin.'

'You see me as ludicrous, don't you?'

He nodded and smiled, tucking her hand under his arm. 'But you've got a lot to be thankful for.

'If I wasn't such a fool.' It was true. She knew now that she loved him desperately when he was coldly and calculatingly considering taking a bride. Someone even Felicia didn't know about. As yet.

CHAPTER SIX

SUSAN was never to forget that trip to Sunset from the moment they flew out of Lara until they dropped anchor in the most beautiful blue lagoon she had ever seen in her life. Outside the reef where the bottom grew shallower, the racing waves had swooped at the yacht's stern, but inside the lagoon it was a glorious calm kingfisher blue.

She stood staring at the island with Emma beside her, excitedly pointing out the landmarks.

'There's the main part of the hotel, reception and the big dining room, and the big building you can see through the palms is the new luxury accommodation. I think I'd like to stay in one of the little bungalows in the grounds, wouldn't you?'

'It looks lovely,' Susan agreed.

'Smasheroo!' Emma seconded in heartfelt tones. She didn't know it, but her mother had wanted to leave her on Lara in Mrs Hansen's care.

'How do we get there?' Susan pointed to the land.

'Someone will come out and get us. Someone from the hotel,' Emma told her. 'The launch tied up at the end of the jetty is the *Island Princess*. She brings tourists over from the mainland. They have a super lunch, wander around the island, buy things from the island shop, then go back again in the afternoon. Uncle Dev is a wonderful sailor, isn't he?'

'Adept at everything!' Susan had to agree, her violet

eyes sweeping along the beautiful yacht, *Sea Mist*. 'He might insist we swim to the shore.'

'Shall we try?' Emma gave a ripple of delighted laughter, a colourful small figure in her yellow shorts and striped T-shirt.

'I even feel we could make it.' Susan was luxuriating in her magical surroundings, the unbelievable blue sea, the horseshoe-shaped island, the coconut palms swaying and the salt breeze tearing through her beautiful, glowing hair and spilling it around her small entranced face.

'Go ahead!' Emma teased her. 'It's too far for me, but you might make it.'

'All right!'

To Emma's astonishment, Susan pulled off her sandals, poised her slender body in its brief shorts and top, then dived in an expert graceful arc into the sparkling lagoon.

'Oh, Susan!' Emma's piercing cry was caught between laughter and shock.

When she surfaced Susan could hear her calling, 'Uncle Dev!' then they were all out on deck looking out at her while she lifted an arm flauntingly, then struck out for the shore. She had never done anything so utterly impulsive before, but the wonder and beauty around her had fired her blood. The water was warm, crystal clear and she felt as happy and buoyant as a dolphin.

An outboard runabout going out to the yacht, slowed beside her, offering assistance, but she waved the young, tow-headed boat-hand on. She was having a wonderful time, even if she had slowed her stroke, and it hadn't even occurred to her to think of sharks. She would love to be first ashore, but the runabout could collect its passengers and easily overtake her.

She didn't look back towards the *Sea Mist*, but forward towards the shore. There were people on the dazzlingly white beach, and sun-worshippers spread out on beach towels on the floating pontoons, and far over on her right a water-skier being pulled over the crystal blue water. She had to stop for a minute to breathe and the runabout swooped in on her and settled alongside.

'Had enough?' Devin called to her, his green eyes brilliant with a faintly derisive amusement.

'No!' She dismissed him with a shake of her water-slicked head.

'Come on, Sue,' Jeff smiled at her, 'I've never seen anything so funny in my life.'

'I tell you I'm quite all right!' She turned up her face to the fabulous sun.

Emma was laughing, crossing her thin little arms across her chest, the boat-hand looked frankly admiring, but Felicia seemed bored to distraction, a silk scarf knotted around her ash-blonde hair. 'You'd look a damn fool if a shark got you,' she said a shade sharply.

'They've never been seen inside the lagoon,' Devin looked hard at her. 'All right, violet eyes,' he turned back to Susan with the sun searing his dark face and deeply tanned torso, 'do you want me to pull you in?'

'I want you to go away and leave me. I can get in under my own steam.'

'Bravo!' Emma put her hands together, smiling at the grinning Jeff. 'It's exciting, isn't it?'

'Take her away!' Devin Chandler turned his dark head carelessly towards the tow-haired young man. 'If this child wants to act like a loony, I'd better join her.'

'But good God, Dev!' Felicia started to remonstrate, but he was already over the side, joining Susan in the sparkling water. Emma was clapping joyously, but she had no chance to join them, for Jeff put his arm around her and the runabout roared away.

'Is it a race, or do we take our time?'

Smiling, he was devastating, his teeth very white, his skin beaded with salt water, his hair setting in close-cropped black curls.

'There's no real danger of sharks, is there?' Her violet eyes were shimmering between her thick water-tipped lashes.

'You should have thought of that before you went over the side.' He reached out a long arm and suddenly ducked her.

They were both submerged beneath the brilliant blue water and he pulled her hard towards him and kissed her salt-water-glossed mouth, kicking them both upwards to the mirror-smooth surface.

'You've got a nerve,' she said breathlessly.

'You shouldn't do unexpected things. It's too easy to make love to you.'

'Isn't it true you're meeting your bride-to-be on the island?'

'It's true!' he returned coolly. 'Don't think I'm like any of your other admirers. I'm different altogether.'

'I'll say!'

Susan thought he was laughing at her, but she didn't want to wait to find out. She turned towards the shore and struck out again, but matching her was child's play to a powerful male swimmer.

'Easy, little one, easy. Let me tow you in.'

'What if I decline the offer?' She tried to retort hotly, but she didn't have the breath for it.

'I promise I'll let you walk in yourself.'

From his voice and his utterly vivid face, he was plainly enjoying himself, still the dominating male, but more relaxed than she had ever seen him.

'Oh, all right!' She gave in because she wanted his arms around her and her lack of stamina was showing.

With his hand beneath her chin they cut cleanly through the water and when they reached the first pontoon he let her go. 'Tell me you're glad I decided to join you.'

'I can't afford not to. It's a lot further than I thought,' she smiled at him, her wet hair a dark red.

'You realise you've earned us an audience?'

'I do!' The beach was lined with spectators watching them. 'Let's hope your mystery lady friend isn't one of them.'

'Why, damn your impertinence!' There was a swift lick of green flame in his brilliant eyes, then she was suddenly swept up into his hard, powerful arms while he carried her through the shallows with the hotel guests on the beach shouting encouragement.

'*Put me down!*'

'Sorry!' He smiled down at her with lazy insolence. 'You're my prisoner.'

'And you're half way a pirate!' She had never seen him in shorts, long brown legs and powerful bare torso matted with dark hair, and it put her in a fever of excitement. He had a superb physique and it had never been more definitely emphasised. 'Please, Dev!'

'That's the first time you've ever used my name.' He ran his eyes over her delicately flushed face. 'All this time and I've never had anything but Mr Chandler or nothing.'

'I'm shy,' she muttered.

'You're enticing.' His voice had the merest lick of sensuality, but it was more than enough for Susan. She gave a little protesting wriggle and he set her down in the ankle-deep water. 'All right, don't panic. You're safe now.'

'I haven't been safe since you found me.'

He laughed and looked away over her head, waving carelessly as a small group on the beach began to clap. 'Here comes Bob,' he told her suavely. 'Don't forget to smile.'

Bob Conrad was hurrying down the beach towards them, bronzed and muscular in cream slacks and a deep blue shirt printed with white hibiscus. 'That was some arrival. I thought I was going to die laughing!' He shook his friend's hand and gave Susan a swift, smiling, appraising glance. 'Welcome to Sunset, Susan. I trust you enjoyed the swim in?'

'I did. It was marvellous, all that glittering turquoise water.'

'And you have days to enjoy it.'

'Thank you. It's very kind of you to ask me.'

'Our pleasure!' He was very pleasant and expansive, but it was obvious he was quietly assessing her. 'Do you mind if I pay you a compliment?'

'Please do.' She smiled at him.

'You're very beautiful.'

'Only one compliment allowed,' Devin Chandler gave his friend a smiling, glinting glance. 'You can see for yourself we're soaked.'

'And I have our best rooms at your disposal,' Bob

Conrad looked back at his friend unabashed. 'Can I be blamed if I like looking at a beautiful young girl?'

Colour was flooding Susan's satiny smooth skin and she looked down at her wet clothes. 'I never thought when I dived in that I'd be complicating things. I'll be trailing water everywhere like a mermaid.'

'Don't worry!' Bob smiled broadly. 'We'll walk back across the gardens to where you're staying. It's our new luxury accommodation. The best of everything, mostly for our overseas guests. Our regulars settle for the lodges where they can step straight out into the water.'

'It's beautiful!' Susan walked between the two men, her eyes revelling in the island scenery. The mountain that rose beyond the hotel complex was covered with gums and pines and palms and tropical flora in profusion and she could imagine herself walking the paths and trails. Couples were strolling along the immaculately kept pathways bordered by majestic palms and frangipani, hibiscus and oleanders in wonderful array, and outside the picturesque self-contained lodges groups of people were relaxing and enjoying one another's company.

The new three-storied luxury block was very impressive, fronting on to the lagoon with a beautiful aquamarine pool at the rear terrace. Guests were lounging on the comfortably upholstered recliners, displaying for the most part gorgeous, golden-tanned bodies, and as they passed by on their way to the ground floor entrance, Susan saw at least four female heads suddenly snap upright, gazing avidly from behind their sunglasses. It was a gala day when such a strikingly handsome male arrived, but Devin Chandler didn't even turn his black lustred head, already by his own admission committed to another woman. An old flame, perhaps? He had told Susan she would be meeting her personally.

'Well now, here we are!' Bob pressed the button as they stepped in the empty lift. 'You're all on the third floor, so you'll have the best view. The others have already been shown up and your gear should be there.'

'Perfect!' Dev glanced down idly at Susan. 'Your hair's drying in ringlets.'

'So's yours.'

'Handsome brute, isn't he?' Bob gave a grunt of laughter. 'More—the only man I've ever truly envied.'

'Rot!'

'True!' Bob answered undaunted. 'Born to money and power, but let me make it plain you could make your fortune anywhere.'

Dev smiled, unimpressed, and as they stepped out of the lift and on to the sundrenched balcony overlooking the pool, Emma raced up to them to fling her arms awkwardly around her uncle's waist. 'Isn't this super?'

'It is!' He took her hand looking down at her, and Felicia emerged from a room a few doors along calling:

'Emma!'

'Here, Mummy.'

'So you've arrived!' Felicia had changed into a brief bra top with a wrap-around skirt and she looked super, casually expensive with a red hibiscus to match the red bra top tucked behind one ear. 'You'd better dry off for a start.'

'That's the idea,' Dev said smoothly, and shepherded them all along the balcony after Bob, who was opening doors.

'You're in here, Susan.'

'Lovely!' She peeped in contentedly and smiled. 'I just don't know how I'm going to thank you.'

'Just keep giving us that sweet smile. Dev, you're at the far end.' The two men moved off together and Bob called to them over his shoulder, 'Settle in and I'll meet you all for a drink before lunch.'

Susan stepped into her room looking around her with pleasure and Felicia and Emma followed.

'Was it necessary for you to make yourself a talking point?' Felicia asked aggressively.

'It was a bit idiotic!' Susan was determined to smile. 'If you'll excuse me I'll change out of these wet clothes.'

'Yes, do. You look a sight, I assure you.' Felicia turned away from examining her own reflection in the full-length mirror set into the door of a row of louvred wardrobes. 'If I may ask a favour of you, would you mind if Emma roomed with you? I'm a very light sleeper at the best of times and she has this irritating snuffle.'

'That's quite all right with me—how about you, Emma?' Susan asked, thinking it was all very strange.

'Actually I'd like to be in a bungalow on the beach,' Emma said confidingly. 'This is all very swanky, but I like the little lodges. You're right on the beach and you can leave your towels and your bathing suits around and everything.'

'Yes, they do look nice.' Susan grabbed a towel from the bathroom, wrapped it around her and walked across to the sliding glass doors, opening them up and walking out on to the balcony. 'If you like we can ask Mr Conrad if there's a lodge available.'

Felicia laughed in amazement. 'If that's what you

want. They're not air-conditioned, but they're cool and comfortable. I'll leave it entirely up to you. Emma, come with me now while Susan is dressing.'

Over a magnificent smorgasbord lunch Susan approached the question of moving into one of the beach-front lodges, but Dev unexpectedly put his foot down.

'You'll be much more comfortable where you are. Besides, I want you right under my nose. Susan can't be expected to go to bed early like Emma and I prefer her to be tucked up safe and sound in the main hotel block.'

So that was the end of it, and Emma accepted the decision gracefully. There was so much to do and see and not half enough time to do it in. Afterwards Dev drew Susan aside for good measure, pointing out that there were lots of other children on the island, all about Emma's age.

'She'll have to learn to communicate with other children,' he said firmly. 'She's been too much with adults for her own good. All kinds of entertainments are arranged for the children and I want her to have fun with her own age group. Apart from helping Emma, it will give you a chance to make your own holiday.'

Susan could see what he meant, but as it happened Emma did make two girl friends and they all insisted on tagging along with Susan as she swam, then started out on one of the scenic walks around the island to Blue Dolphin Point. As a teacher children had been part of her life and the natural warmth and humour that was in her made children of all ages respond. Emma was improving a lot and the three little girls' chatter and enthusiasm made their excursions all the more enjoyable. Jeff and Felicia seemed content to lounge beside the pool sipping drinks between cool plunges and Dev had disappeared with the Conrads to be shown over all the improvements to the complex and the new helicopter landing pad.

With nightfall Emma had a natural desire to fall asleep, but Susan dressed excitedly for the evening's entertainment. There were all sorts of 'nights' arranged when the guests dressed appropriately if they felt like it, and the South Sea Island Night made it easy. In the Island shop she had found an alluring Polynesian sarong in a combination of peacock colours and it made the most of her colouring and her soft, silky shoulders and arms.

'What about a flower for your hair?' Emma suggested critically.

'What would you suggest?' Susan glanced at Emma's small, reclining figure behind her.

'How about a gardenia? There's a bush downstairs covered in them.' She bounced off the bed so purposefully, Susan protested:

'You can't go, not in your pyjamas. I don't suppose anyone will mind if I pick a few.'

'Oh, you must!' Emma insisted. 'It'll be the finishing touch!'

Downstairs in the garden Susan easily located the big glossy-leafed shrub, its flowers gleaming, its perfume spreading its sweetness on the burnished night. Defty she broke off two blooms with a little foliage, not seeing anyone until she was back in the building, waiting for the lift. After a minute it descended and two young men got out, dressed for the night life in pale slacks and island shirts, their bright eyes focusing on Susan as if they had found a vision.

'Wow!'

'Hi! This is an unhoped-for pleasure!'

They advanced on her, their expressions so easy to read that she at last accepted she was beautiful. 'Hello!' she smiled at them, sweet as honey, but gently reserved.

'Chuck Summers....'

'Bill Fredricks....'

They waited for her to introduce herself while the lift went away again.

'Susan Blake.'

They both bowed, renewing their smiles. 'Delighted to meet you. The future looks glorious!' Chuck seemed to be the spokesman and he looked down at the flowers in her hand. 'You're staying on for the cabaret?'

'I hope to.'

'You think then we could join you?'

'Actually....' Susan watched as the lift door opened and Devin emerged, head down, deep in thought until he saw her and her companions.

'Good evening!' His green eyes touched each young man in turn. 'I just came to see what had happened to you, Susan.'

'Emma thought I needed a gardenia.' She was faintly bemused at the sight of him, but her young admirers apparently decided to take off, Chuck with a rueful wave of his hand. 'See you later!'

They were together and the warm evening breeze was making the air beautiful. 'Oh, Susan!' Devin glanced down at her coolly, very tall, wide-shouldered, lean-hipped, like an athlete.

'What's that supposed to mean?' She was feeling slightly giddy just looking up at him. 'Were you really looking for me?'

'As a matter of fact I was. What were those two do-ing, paying you compliments?'

'How clever of you!' Mischief made her say the first thing that came into her head. 'They're hoping to join me later on this evening.'

'Oh, there are a lot of things they can hope for, but they'd better put the idea aside.'

'Why? I'm over twenty-one.'

'Not relevant.' He took her arm and drew her back into the lift. 'I must point out to you that to my mind you're just a sweet little girl who needs protection.'

'Yes, from *you*!' Her violet eyes flashed.

'So make the best of it!' He was considering her with interest and a mocking amusement. 'In the morn-ing I'm taking you out in the catamaran.'

'I thought you were waiting for the future Mrs Chandler to arrive.'

'That's not very polite and I don't want you to tell anyone. It's off the record.'

'I find it hard to believe you're thinking of taking a wife at all,' she challenged him without looking up.

'But surely I told you why? It's not for myself it's for Lara.'

'How awful! If she loves you she's bound to die of a broken heart.'

They were on the balcony again and he followed her to the door, tapping on it and calling Emma's name.

'Oh, you got the gardenias, that's good!' Emma was at the door in an instant, moving back to allow them in-side. 'Doesn't Susan look beautiful, Uncle Dev?'

'A flower in a celestial field,' he said mockingly. 'Try one behind each ear. Have a nice day, baby?' He moved to smile at Emma.

'Super! We were on the go all the time. We met up with two friends and walked half way around the island.'

'How energetic!'

'One's father is a doctor, the best surgeon in the world, and Michelle's father writes songs or words or something.'

'Actually, dear, he's well known. Nick McDonough,' Susan told her, driving a hairpin through a flower.

'They both took a fancy to Susan. They told me. Being so pretty helps, of course, but she's so kind and funny.'

'True enough, I suppose.' Dev was looking at Susan, his smile a little taut, the brilliance of his eyes quite devastating. 'I think a little television until eight o'clock, then bed, young Emma.'

'It's all right, I'm quite sleepy. I'm going for a swim as soon as I get up in the morning.'

'Then let Susan sleep in. Someone is always on the beach to watch you and I get up early wherever I am.'

'Right, it's a date!' Emma whirled back and flopped on the bed. 'Is Mummy coming in to say goodnight to me?'

'I'm quite sure she is,' her uncle reassured her. 'We'll give her another ten minutes, then we'll all walk over together.'

Dinner was superb in beautiful surroundings and afterwards they moved to the cabaret room where a talented group were pouring out disco music.

'Expensive but good!' Trish Conrad murmured in Susan's ear. 'There's more to running a hotel these days than there ever was before. Once it was the beauty of the reef, good fishing and good food, now everyone likes to play until the small hours. We have a hideaway at the point of the island to take special care of the night owls so they won't disturb the other guests.'

'Yes, I saw it this afternoon.' Bob Conrad held her chair and she slipped in to it, the lei of gingerblossom around her neck swinging forward. 'That was an absolute feast!'

Trish nodded, smiling. 'It's lovely to see you enjoying yourself and you've been so good with Emma. Bless you for it, dear!'

There was a lot of talking and laughter around them and a lot of interested glances. Nearly all of the guests were aware that the Conrads owned the island resort and there was some speculation as to the identity of their guests.

After a few moments Jeff asked Felicia to dance and she stood up coolly and smiled at him: 'Love to,' adding something else when they were both out of earshot. Bob Conrad put a tall frosted glass in front of Susan, but she made no attempt to drink it. She had seen her brother's face, smooth enough for most people, but an agony for his sister. So far as Felicia was concerned, Jeff was suffering from an overriding physical attraction, and this holiday on the island was throwing them together almost as equals.

'Susan!' Dev repeated her name.

'I beg your pardon?' she answered vaguely.

'I don't think this child is exactly at ease with me,' he smiled at Trish, who smiled back at him.

'I don't find that strange. Remember you're the big cattle baron with a certain amount of looks and money.'

'Thanks, Trish!' He finished his drink and held out

his hand. 'Come dance with me as a punishment.'

'What a light penalty!'

They moved out on to the dance floor and Bob Conrad smiled at Susan. 'I can hardly believe the change in young Emma. Dev tells me it's your doing.'

'Then he's underrating his own influence. Emma loves him dearly.'

'And what about you?'

She must have started because he put out his hand, patting her wrist. 'Frankly I'm delighted. Dev needs a wife.'

'Perhaps so,' she protested a little wildly, 'but *I* don't come into his plans at all. I mean, I'm not right. I don't know why you find it so acceptable. He would have to marry someone who could fit into his particular way of life. As far as he's concerned I'm just a child and my background is very ordinary.'

'There's nothing ordinary about you,' he assured her. 'I didn't meant to upset you, Susan. I like you and I'd like to get to know you better. Dev is my friend. I really care about him.'

'Then I'm surprised you don't know he's thinking seriously of getting married.' She looked across the room to the dance floor to where he was dancing with Trish. Her soft, pretty mouth was quivering with laughter and she was looking up at him with a touching warmth. Devin Chandler, a man apart.

'I daresay you mean Felicia,' Bob muttered, after a pause. 'It's incredible, utterly incredible. I remember them all in the days before Felicia got herself into the family. In my opinion, little Susan, you want to keep an eye on your brother. Felicia likes collecting scalps without really concerning herself with the heartache she causes.'

'She told me she's in love with Dev and she means to marry him,' Susan said quietly.

'It's not on!' Bob said brusquely. 'Whatever Dev thinks of his sister-in-law, marriage to her isn't on his mind. I've already told you I know the whole story from way back. The brothers were so different you could hardly believe it, yet Brad was a nice guy—too nice for Felicia. Forgive me, but I know this will go no further. I've never liked Flick and she knows it. Trish doesn't like her either, but she's much too nice a person to let Felicia know it. I'm just a bumbling country boy who can't hide his feelings all that much.'

'Neither can I, apparently,' Susan smiled shakily.

'Ah, but not everyone is studying you so closely, Susan,' he said kindly. 'Cool as he is, I still know Dev well enough to guess at his true feelings. He's a hard-headed man who endured a very painful upbringing. I don't think he trusts women all that much or expects any real companionship out of a marriage. If you're wondering about his motive in asking Felicia out to Lara, it was for the child. Felicia's not the type for mothering. In fact she shocked Trish by telling her she loathed the job. It's our great sorrow that we haven't been able to have children.'

'I'm sorry!' Impulsively Susan touched his hand. 'Really, I'm most terribly sorry.'

'Yet our marriage will last,' he smiled at her. 'Trish is the best part of me and we've come round to thinking about adoption.'

'Then you *will* have your family.'

'A man has to work for something.' He leaned back in

his chair, staring at her. 'What is it about Dev that frightens you—his world, or his success or his aura? I know he can be somewhat daunting at different times. But then he has to be.'

'I've never met anyone like him in my life.' She infused a world of feeling into the single sentence. 'But I'm just an ordinary mortal, Mr Conrad. . . .'

'Bob,' he corrected.

'And he really hasn't looked at me at all.'

'You don't really mean that?' He looked back at her very dryly. 'Dev has a great eye for beauty and I bet there are plenty of women in this room who wish they had just a fraction of what you've got.'

'You're too kind to me,' Susan said wryly. 'Mrs Chandler is the one who turns heads.'

'Ah yes, she is beautiful, but what she is, the coldness, the arrogance, is also branded on her face. She's only been here a day, yet already the staff know her. Felicia gives herself over to being unpleasant to those she doesn't consider important. I can understand your brother's attraction. In all likelihood he's never met a woman like Felicia before, but he's only part of her high strategy. Probably she's only trying to make Dev jealous.'

'Then she'll have to do a great deal to break through that sardonic charm.' By this time Susan had reached for her glass, finding the cold drink anything but repugnant. 'So far as I'm concerned your instincts were right. I'm hopelessly in love with him.' She even trembled at the force of her emotion. 'But he told me himself, rather gently really, that he had someone definitely in mind. It's time for him now to take a wife. For Lara. It sounds such a terrible, coldblooded thing to do.'

'And you think Dev's coldblooded?' Bob gave a shout of laughter that turned heads.

'I know he is!' She made an agitated little movement of her hands.

'You don't, as it happens,' Bob countered dryly. 'Dev is a man of strong passions even if he keeps them well under control.'

'They're coming back now,' Susan warned him quickly. 'I've told Dev I'm going home after this holiday.'

'And what did he say?'

'I think he's going to give me a bon voyage party.' She leant back in her comfortable armchair as Dev and Trish rejoined them, with Felicia and Jeff wending their way through the tables. There were all kinds of complications in life and both she and Jeff were already in over their heads.

When Dev asked her to dance she declined sweetly, saying she was rather tired, then committed the unforgivable sin later in the evening by dancing with the persistent Chuck Summers. He was clearly attracted and he helped to take her mind off what was happening right under her nose. Felicia was very cleverly using Jeff to get her brother-in-law's attention and Susan found it very hard to watch it.

The evening came to an end in the cabaret room after an excellent floor show and Felicia suggested they go on to the hideaway. They all declined, even Jeff, and Felicia put her hand imperiously on his arm, looking faintly outraged. 'You actually want to have an early night?'

'No, no.' He shrugged and looked at the others.

'Then come with me. All I need is one male and Dev seems unwilling.'

'It's quite simple,' her brother-in-law answered levelly. 'I want to be up in time to take Emma for a swim.'

Felicia gave a contemptuous little click of her tongue. 'I would say you're up before dawn every day of your life.'

Trish looking faintly embarrassed, leaned over and kissed Susan's cheek. 'I'll say goodnight, dear. See you in the morning.'

'Goodnight, Trish.' Susan smiled at her. 'I've enjoyed myself.'

'And how did you get rid of young Chuck exactly?' Bob looked at her.

'I told him I always retire early.'

'Very well then, Jeff,' Felicia said languidly, 'let's go.'

A minute later, the goodnights over, Susan was out in the night air, with Dev's hand hard at her elbow.

'If you're so tired, would you like me to carry you home?' he asked.

'Well,' she said a little angrily, 'I've been brought up properly. You told me yourself you'd found the woman you intended to make your wife.'

'I've no one to answer to, as yet,' he returned suavely. 'I didn't realise you were such a capricious little witch. There were times tonight I could have given you a good shake. No trouble at all.'

'The joke is I didn't want to dance with Chuck.'

'You seemed to be making him completely happy.'

'Where are we heading for?' The minutes were passing like a reverie and now she could see they were taking the path to the beach.

'Not to ruin, as you seem to think.'

'Please, Dev!' A growing excitement was taking possession of her. 'I want to go in, not go for a walk.'

'Hush!' he soothed her. 'The night air will make you sleep.'

The most beautiful balmy breeze blew in from the surf, white-capped beyond the dazzling silver shimmer of the glassy lagoon. The long fronds of the giant coconuts waved like sentinels above them and the water lapped rhythmically on the fine white sand. It was overwhelmingy romantic and Susan even had the mad desire to take off her clothes and swim for a long time in the moon-drenched water. Here in the scented darkness Devin would be beside her and she could indulge an unreality.

The wind whipped at her sarong, lining it against her slender body, a body that had come tinglingly alive. If he touched her he would know she had no armour against him, no strength, no wisdom. She only knew what was in her heart.

He held her arm and she pulled away from him, running ahead, drifting on the wind. The ginger blossom lei was still around her neck and when she reached the rocky arm that enclosed the calm lagoon she moved across the smooth boulders and threw the ring of flowers out on to the tide.

'Susan!' His arm was around her, pulling her back to the coral strand. 'I thought you were going to leap off for a moment.'

'Would you follow me?' The role of temptress was new to her, yet she was playing at it recklessly.

'I have this far.' He gave a brief, hard laugh. 'Sometimes I think you don't consider the consequence of your actions.'

'Only with you because you're so strong.' Without her sandals she was very small and to make herself feel more equal she stood up again on a rock. 'Dare I invite the lash of your anger?'

'Who's angry?' He put out his hands and held her by her narrow hips.

'Like this, I can look into your eyes,' she said with an intense seriousness.

'Are you sure you're ready for it?' His voice was edged with some feeling that held her motionless.

'I'm blind so far as you're concerned. I'll always remember that you saved my life, but if I let you I know you'll wound me.'

'Maybe I would,' he said harshly. 'You need cherishing if you're going to survive. Just an ivory figurine with lapis lazuli eyes.'

'Then let me have my freedom!' she cried swiftly. 'You know what you're doing, just holding me in the palm of your hand while you're waiting for some other woman.'

'You little fool!'

Even as she was reeling, losing her balance, he picked her up in his arms, carrying her back towards the grove of pandanus, while she turned her face into his throat, shrivelled by his anger, desolate. . . .

'I love you!' The words were torn out of her, but so softly he might never have heard them. She clasped her arms around his neck as if she were drowning, so ensnared it would take five lives to forget him.

Somehow they were on the sand and his hands were

moving over her as if she were silk. 'Say it again.'

'What?' Her voice was a mere whisper, reduced by sensation.

'That you love me.' His voice seemed to mock her, even as the hands that cupped her breasts held a tender domination.

'Why are you being so cruel?' she jerked out, terrified of the pleasure his hands were giving her.

'Because I want you,' he said in a hard voice. 'For a long time now, since I found you under my tree in the rain forest. I don't even like what you're doing to me, weaving tendrils all around me, sapping my strength.'

'Then send me away!' She tried to move, but his arms imprisoned her.

'Maybe I don't want to be free of you,' he told her, low-voiced. 'Your grace and your beauty, the funny little spurts of anger. Life can be very barren, very hard without a woman.'

'Oh, please let me *go*!' She was beginning to feel frantic, held helpless, yet burning with desire. 'I can't begin to understand you. You say you want me, yet you've made plans for your life.'

'Yes.' He touched his mouth to her breast, burning it through the thin cotton material. 'It would be one hell of a mistake to lock you into my life. You're too young and you're too vulnerable. I'm a good deal harder than anyone else you've known.'

'And you take what you want as though you're entitled to it!' She was suddenly seized with a wild kind of anger. The sheer arrogance of him to propose to take her like a chattel. She was a woman. A *woman*, in a world everywhere threatened by men. Cruel, biting, powerful men who never took a woman seriously.

'Stop that!' His arms came about her, small and slighty hysterical, strugging against him, her eyes full of tears. 'I have to be careful not to hurt you, you're so small. Anyway, you've been leading me on for most of the night. You might have expected to suffer some consequences.'

Susan caught her breath sharply, suddenly still, but he had found her mouth, possessing it as if he hungered for its sweetness, as if he could never get enough of it. He was the embodiment of power and mastery, setting her rigid body free so that it became something they both wanted. To be a woman, desired, was an incomparable delight, but still he didn't speak one word of love, or press an advantage even as he blotted her every defence out of her mind.

The remaining days passed in a golden haze of beauty. Susan had the distinct feeling she was dreaming and would soon have to wake up. When she was almost ready to deny him nothing, Dev had turned into an indulgent, oddly congenial companion, relaxed and charming and exciting enough to tear her heart, but after that one night when he had made love to her until she was shaking in his arms, there was never a moment when he acted remotely like a lover. Her enslavement might never have happened, and if he often caught her wide, startled eyes on him, he chose to ignore their violet bewilderment.

But there were compensations galore. Each day was crowded with glorious activity. They cruised all around the other beautiful islands; viewed the dazzling colour and wonder of the coral gardens; the brilliantly coloured tropical fish that swam in shoals through the fantastic blue world. They left one morning very early for some deep sea fishing, black marlin, Spanish mackerel, bonito and bluefin; then spent some incredible hours skindiving in an exquisitely colourful underwater world. It was the finest holiday Susan had ever had in her life and she glowed as if a fire had been lit inside her.

Felicia didn't join in their daytime adventures. She had little interest in coral gardens and tropical fish and she swore that long hours in the water ruined the skin. Trish, as a good hostess, often offered to stay with her, but by now Felicia had a host of admirers to encircle her as she lazed beside the pool.

To Susan's enormous relief, Jeff fought free of her fascination for a good part of the time. He was enjoying the underwater wonderland as much as anything in his life, and when he fought a black king and won, he professed himself sold on the pleasures of big game fishing. It was in the evenings that Felicia came into her own. She had brought a stunning wardrobe of resort clothes and she turned every head each evening she swept into the dining room. With Dev so obviously treating Susan as a guest to be indulged, all her tensions had relaxed. After lazing like a lizard all day in the sun, Felicia became very lively company at night. Then Dev was responding to her, his green eyes alight, and certainly he was a wonderful man. He meant so much to her, she could even remain faithful. Such was the message in her long, almond eyes.

On their last evening Susan was thrown into a minor panic when she found her name listed for the talent quest. It was Emma, of course, and even as she whirled to withdraw, Felicia's acid bantering more than anything decided her on remaining in. No one expected a professional performance from amateurs, indeed the sheer amateurishness was part of the fun.

As it happened, though her knees were shaking with nervousness, she was a very real surprise to her audience. They loved her, and afterwards Nick McDonough wandered over to their table to congratulate her and ask her if she would sing again.

'If you do, I'll accompany you.'

'Lovely,' she agreed, laughing. He played the guitar much better than she did, and to compliment him in turn she later sang one of his songs, with Chuck Summers standing up at his table and shouting 'Bravo!' No one seemed to mind in the least losing to her and when Nick took her place on the high stool to entertain them with three songs it really crowned a highly successful evening. Only Felicia looked at her with disapproval as though she was nothing but an extrovert, but Dev stood up and in front of everyone kissed her cheek and dropped another lei of wild orchids over her glowing, curly head.

When Emma found out in the morning she jumped up and hugged her, but there was no time to chat. They were leaving that morning under power and Emma, yelling with laughter, wanted one more swim.

CHAPTER SEVEN

THEIR arrival back on Lara coincided with a severe tropical storm, the first of the season and a good indication that the bad weather was coming. They had flown through a threatening sky; now, a scant hour after they had touched down with the Beech Baron secure in its hangar, the sun disappeared from the purple-black sky and the thunder and lightning began.

Parrots screeched loudly and flew for cover not a moment before a great wind sprang up out of nowhere and the rain came down, solid silver sheets of it that obliterated the garden and set up such a drumming on the roof, one had to shout to be heard.

'Be careful, Susan, you'll get all wet!' Emma was calling to her over the howling wind. The rain was driving on to the verandah, but still Susan stood mesmerised by so much naked power. The thunder rolled and the lightning slashed through the livid banks of clouds, so brilliant it seared her eyes.

'*Susan!*' She turned her head to see Emma gesturing wildly. 'Come in!'

'Not a chance! This is fantastic.'

'You're all wet.'

'No matter!' The world all around them was filled with turbulent motion, rain and wind and the lashing trees. She had never seen anything like it, and her voice sounded weak against the howling fury of the storm.

She held on to the white railing with both hands, rain
shrouding her, its impact softened by the deep over-
hang that protected the verandah.

Emma hurried back into the house and a minute
later Devin came out on to the verandah, taking a firm
grip on Susan's shoulders. 'Haven't I got enough head-
aches?' he demanded.

'What am I doing wrong?' She allowed herself to be
drawn backwards.

'You're frightening Emma out of her wits, for one
thing.'

'Surely not!' She hadn't even considered that aspect.

'Most people are terrified of storms.' With an almost
violent motion he ran his hand over her damp head,
curling tightly with all the moisture in the atmosphere.
'If you want to do the right thing for the next hour at
least you can help close the shutters and keep an eye on
Emma. Unlike you, she's not feeling the same flame of
wonder.'

'All right,' she said angrily, 'I have closed the shutters, as it happens.'

'Then you haven't noticed your room. The water's
running in fast.'

'Damn, I'm sorry.' She made a little sound of annoy-
ance. 'It just seemed so wild and beautiful.'

'Remarkably at times, the description seems to fit
you!' They were inside her room and he secured the
shutters, then the French doors, looking around at her.
'One of these days I'll let you sit out a storm, seeing
you're so at home in the tropical world, but not now.
All this racket is making Emma hide. Come on, let's get
you dried out.' He walked through to the adjoining
bathroom and came back with a towel.

She tried to pull it off him, but he told her pretty briskly: 'Let it alone.'

The next minute he was rubbing her hair dry while she moaned softly and finally reeled against him. 'You'll rub it off!'

'Have you ever had a summer cold? They're hard to get rid of.'

'I never catch cold at all,' she shrugged.

'Well, well!' He released his iron grip and draped the towel around her neck. 'Another mark in your favour.' His inflexible expression had given way to amusement as he looked down at her. 'I've never seen the like of your hair. I missed all those Shirley Temple movies.'

'It's an affliction to me too.'

'Not a bit, it's beautiful! Now would you be so good as to calm little Emma, seeing you're our resident witch.'

'Not for long,' she shot back at him. 'If I stay here, I'm awfully afraid you'll have your way with me.'

'You mean you'd let me?' His mouth twisted in a smile.

'I've considered the matter, and the answer's *no*.'

'Is that a challenge?' His green eyes sprang to life.

'No!' Her small face sobered and she turned away. 'A very good idea. For everything you've done for me, I thank you, but it's time to go home.'

'All right!' He sounded very brisk and businesslike. 'Let it lie there for the moment. I've got other things on my mind and you can make yourself useful. Emma is out in the kitchen with Jess. Go along and reassure her of your physical wellbeing. It's important to her.'

Susan didn't say anything but moved over to the chest of drawers searching out some dry clothes. Whatever was between them he could dismiss her with the utmost calm.

It rained steadily until midnight and they were all up early to see how much damage had been done. Trees had been planted all round the house as a natural cyclone break and though the ground was heavy with moisture and fallen petals of all colours carpeted the grass no tree or shrub had been uprooted.

Harry Tindall and Jeff called up to the house with their report and a half hour later Dev rode out, pre-occupied and uncommunicative. If the rain came, they'd be laid up for days, weeks, and the air was sultry with heat. A low pressure area had been officially reported as building up in the Gulf and it had already begun to affect their weather. The golden halcyon days were over and the North prepared for the Wet.

Felicia thought it opportune to acquaint Susan with the exact position, starting in the moment Dev had left the house. Susan was in her room, staring out at the garden, when she tapped on the door and entered.

'Emma?' Susan didn't turn her heard, thinking it was the child.

'No, it's not,' Felicia answered coolly. 'She's with Mrs Hansen at the moment. You and I are going to have a little talk.'

'How lovely!' Susan turned around with deliberate slowness while Felicia sank into an armchair, crossed her long slender legs and drew them to one side.

'Don't be cute with me,' she said swiftly. 'We had an agreement, remember?'

'You mean when you gave me my marching orders?'

'Precisely!' Felicia picked up an ornament, looked

at it, and put it down beside her. 'The holiday's over, my dear. There's no future for you here, in fact a very disagreeable time. Don't think that storm last night meant nothing. It's the start of the Wet—a very dismal period, I can tell you, before the sky's clear again.'

'Then shouldn't you leave too?' Susan asked sweetly. 'I should imagine you'd find it very hard to take.'

'That's my business,' Felicia retorted, very steady and cool. 'Let's come to grips with yours. If you delay too long, you won't be able to get out. Cyclones are quite common at this time of the year and some of them can be particularly violent. There's one battering the Western Australia coast right now. Our turn may be next and Dev's needed for far more important things than trying to ferry out a guest who stayed too long.'

'I realise that,' Susan said. 'Don't worry, Mrs Chandler, I've already spoken to Dev about leaving.'

'Well, good for you!' Felicia answered almost agreeably. 'There's no point in waiting until the rain starts, we must arrange something now.'

'I'll leave it to Dev,' said Susan.

'Pardon me, you won't!' Felicia drew in her legs as if she meant to stand up, but remained there. 'Dev will have enough on his hands. I can arrange for a small charter plane to be flown in. It will take you to the coast and you can find your own way from there. I assume you have money?'

'Not much, but enough.' Susan closed her eyes. She couldn't help it. The sense of loss ... *loss* ... was assailing her and she had to cling tightly to her pride.

'You're in love with him, aren't you?' Felicia exclaimed maliciously. 'I'm sorry, of course. It's a humiliating experience, but fairly normal. Dev always was terribly attractive to women, even without his money. My husband left very little to me, did you know? It all goes to Emma. Dev is her guardian.'

Susan held up her hand. 'You don't have to talk to me about your business, Mrs Chandler.'

'I thought you should know the kind of man I married. I won't make that mistake again.' Felicia vowed bitterly. 'I've told you from the beginning I want Dev. Everyone else bores me by comparison.'

'Really?' Susan couldn't resist it. 'I thought you'd taken a small interest in my brother.'

'I beg your pardon?' Felicia's eyes flickered.

'You may well prefer to deny it. You're a beautiful woman and it's not for me to comment on your methods. Except I'd like you to leave my brother alone.'

'You're crazy!' Felicia glowered at her and stood up. 'I consider your attitude offensive. It's inconceivable that I'd be interested in your brother—a graceless boy.'

'I'm glad to hear it,' Susan continued bravely. 'Jeff is just going through the stage where he prefers older women.'

'You bitch!' Felicia hissed emotively. 'I won't forget that little barb. By the same token you ought to take a good look at your own leanings. You're the worse of the two, just a cheap little nobody aiming for the stars.'

'Anything else?' Susan asked, suddenly weary.

'Get your things together!' Felicia stalked to the door. 'It's a mistake to be pretentious. You'd never fit in here, in Dev's world. I've known it since childhood. I understand Dev and deep down he knows it. I even go along with this absurd mystique about Lara. Dev's the man I should have married in the first place.'

'How did it happen you didn't?' Susan moved away to the dressing table and began brushing her hair.

'A form of cruelty!' Felicia gave a high, thin laugh. 'Dev and I have always been cruel to each other.' She turned to smile at Susan over her shoulder. 'Now don't waste time, pack your things. The fact is, Dev's a bit embarrassed about asking you to leave.'

In spite of her misery Susan laughed. 'He's not the kind of man to be embarrassed by anything, but you've made your point, Mrs Chandler. Lay off my brother and I'll leave.'

'My dear girl,' Felicia gave a triumphant little laugh, 'I don't give a damn for your brother. You must know that very well. Dev loved me once and he'll love me again.'

It seemed absolutely essential to get out of the house. Though it upset Susan that she could no longer support Emma with her friendship, it was clear she had to go. Felicia was the child's mother and she had all the rights, whether she behaved like a poor sort of mother or not. It was so undignified to exchange insults and she couldn't continue to put herself in a position where she could expect them. Dev himself had raised the question of marriage and it was shockingly clear that he had meant Felicia all along. Even Bob Conrad had thought as much, though he had his misgivings. For one thing it would solve the problem of Emma and give the highly erotic Felicia exquisite satisfaction. The thought of her with Devin was like being put on the rack or going through hell, but Susan well knew he was an experienced man with a sensual technique he hadn't gained overnight. There had been enough hints about their love affair in the past, and Felicia wouldn't be in the least difficult to get into bed with. Eventually there would be an heir, the strong, handsome son Felicia wanted and a cattle empire demanded. Devin Chandler was hard, super efficient and resolute. He had his plans all laid out.

Susan had been riding aimlessly for about twenty minutes before she encountered Rick Gardiner returning to camp. They had been mustering the horses since early morning and he looked tired and irritable.

'How goes it, sweetheart?'

'Hello, Rick.' She held Silky in while he rode up to her. 'I've just been looking at the storm damage.'

'That was a really heavy fall.' He was looking her over carefully, devouring her, really. 'Jeff's been full of his trip to the Reef. What about you?'

'I had a wonderful time.'

'I bet!' He gave a hard little laugh. 'You look good, really good, but I'll tell you why you're a little fool. Put Chandler out of your mind completely and finally. My God, you're a pretty girl, you don't have to run after anyone.'

'And I don't have to listen to your jealous abuse,' she countered unsteadily, feeling beset on all sides.

'Why not?' His narrowed eyes challenged her unpleasantly. 'I'm not making any headway trying to be pleasant. I took a fancy to you from the very first moment, but you haven't given me a chance. I know that very well—and I know why. I'm young and I'm healthy and I'm pretty damned presentable, but I haven't got enough money. Or class. Chandler's big in both departments. Even my dad falls down adoring, but not me. I'm not killing myself for nothing. If you hadn't set your cap at Chandler, I'd have suited you very well.'

'You're mistaken!' She was stammering, perturbed by the pitch of his anger and self-pity.

'And you're a silly little fool!' He suddenly reached for her, got a hand to her nape and kissed her mouth so grindingly, the soft, tender inner part of her lip sprang a few beads of blood.

'Go on, hate me!' he urged desperately. 'It's better than nothing!'

'Let me *go*!' She was shocked to the extent she kicked the little mare into action. It shied and looked around nervously, then sprang away at a gallop, mane flying, swinging right.

Susan heard Rick shout after her and she drew a little sobbing breath. She wanted to cry bitterly, wildly, with Emma's abandon, but she had brought this all on herself. The farcical aspects of her life suddenly appalled her. She had no justification for remaining on Lara at all. She *was* a fool, and worse, if she allowed herself to submit to a humiliating situation. Love was an illusion, none bigger, and a catastrophe when it was one-sided.

She was galloping clear of a fallen limb when to her horror it sprang to life, rushing the mare with short, powerful legs. She lashed out wildly, but it ran up the mare's leg almost to the chest, clinging ferociously—a huge, yellow-mottled brown monitor with a long reptilian head. She couldn't help it, she screamed, and the little mare reared in terror throwing her forward over its head. Into blackness.

She awoke to pain, with her ribs strapped and a large bump on her skull. She was in her own bed and Devin was bending over her, his face grimmer than she had ever seen it.

'Where does it hurt?'

'Everywhere!' she gasped with the pain. 'I thought I was going to die, everything happened so fast.'

'It usually does,' he agreed humourlessly. 'I have to feed you some painkillers when you feel able to take them. You've got a cracked rib and an almighty bump on your head, but otherwise you're not too bad.'

'Thanks.' She tried to smile.

'*Don't!*' he said sharply. 'You can't imagine what it was like seeing you lying there.'

'And Silky?' Her eyes darkened with remembered horror.

'Don't worry about Silky.' His expression was soothing. 'I've taken care of her. You have to have complete rest for a couple of days.'

'And who strapped me up?' She tried to move further up in the bed and winced when she couldn't.

'Joe Grant. He's flown in and out. We were thinking of shifting you to hospital for observation but decided you might as well stay here in your own bed. I can watch for any signs.'

'Such as?'

'Nausea. Blood. I can fly you out at the least sign of trouble. If not, Joe will be here in a couple of days just to check you over.'

'Tell me it could have happened to anyone,' she begged. 'It was like a horrible nightmare.'

'I think you must have ridden right into it.' He shook a couple of capsules into his hand and half filled a glass of water. 'Gardiner made a couple of mistakes today. He'll be disciplined for it. 'I'm sorry.'

'Then you saw it?' Susan was whispering, her eyes enormous in a pale, bruised face.

'*I* didn't, otherwise I might have beaten him up. Two of the men were riding that way. One went to your assistance and the other reported back to me on the double. By the time I got there you were a heart-rending sight and Gardiner so shocked it would have been an extra cruelty to have flattened him.' He came to stand beside the bed, looking down at her, his dark face drawn tight, the chiselled, clearly defined mouth compressed into a narrow line. 'Let's get these pain-killers down, shall we?'

'I don't really want them, I think I'll be sick.' She looked back at him with a helpless air, but he sank down on to the bed beside her.

'Joe told me you'd need them. I'm sorry, little one, but we'll have to chance the nausea. You must have the devil's own headache.'

She heard the unfamiliar tenderness in his voice and the tears swam in her eyes. 'You must rue the day our paths crossed.'

Typically, he didn't answer her but held her firmly and gently while she swallowed the capsules. 'You don't have to stay with me,' she protested weakly. 'Leave me alone with my miseries. I'll be all right.'

'I think I'll stay all the same. The young heal quickly, that's my only consolation.'

'You're a strange man,' she gave a little wry smile and closed her eyes, responding to the sedation. 'There's nothing I can do at the moment, is there?'

'No, just stay with me.'

The words came from a distance off, but still she heard them. Devin knew she loved him and perhaps he

was sad for her. She seemed to be in less pain, floating . . . floating. Her heavy lashes settled, but still he
kept vigil.

She awoke a couple of times during the night and
he was there beside her in an armchair, listening to her
ramblings, offering her medication, bathing her face
and her hands and changing the pillow slips because
she had broken out into a sweat. She wanted him there
badly and she must have told him, because when she
went back to sleep again, he was holding her hand, his
face in the dull glow of the table lamp a dark gold, lines
of strain about the eyes and the mouth. It would have
been a terrible thing to have a dead girl on his property.
That would account for the strange tension in him.
The way he was studiously looking after her. She
couldn't bear to know.

Sunshine was slanting across the verandah when she
opened her eyes again. Jess Hansen had put a breakfast
tray down on the table and was now hovering beside
her, the anxious expression on her face giving way to
pure joy as soon as she saw Susan open her eyes.

'Well now, you're awake! How are you feeling,
love?'

Her voice was warm and deep-throated and Susan
smiled, but made no attempt to move. She felt as
thought Silky had trampled her, but she didn't want to
complain when Jess was looking so pleased.

'Hungry, love?'

'I don't think so, Jess.'

'Come on. You'll feel better if you have something,'
Jess looked at her coaxingly. 'Something light—a little
juice, scrambled egg. It'll just slip down. I made tea

and coffee, so you can take your pick.'

'You're too good to me, Jessie.' Despite her efforts to be brave the tears came to her eyes.

'Don't cry, love, there's a good girl!' Jess said bracingly. 'Such a dreadful day we had yesterday. Take my word for it, Mr Chandler was nearly out of his mind. But afterwards Dr Grant was able to calm him down. You looked so small and helpless, like a little wax doll, and your breathing was awful.'

'I'm sorry I had to give everyone such a fright!' Instinctively Susan's hand went out and the housekeeper took it, patting it, half way between dismay and happiness.

'You were lucky, child.'

'I'm not such a good rider, I'm afraid,' Susan sighed.

'You have to know what to look for. Those goannas will climb anything. I remember years ago, one of them ran at a visitor and nearly gave him a heart attack. There are always hazards in the bush, love, and snakes. They'll go for a horse and rider. Now, what about some breakfast? I'll have to get word to your brother and the Tindalls. All of us have been so anxious. Your brother will want to come across and see you. I daresay, Mary as well. Feel up to it?'

'Just give me an hour,' Susan croaked, then gasped as she tried to move. 'I don't recommend cracked ribs.'

'No, dear,' Jess clucked sympathetically. 'Now let me help you. You can depend upon having young Emma here in a moment!'

With a little breakfast in her, Susan felt better and able to cope with Emma's lamentations. She had given the child a shock at a time when Emma was still getting over her father's tragic death and she couldn't help but feel penitent. Emma sat in the armchair, very pale and dark-eyed, and Susan suggested she go out to the kitchen for the glass of milk she hadn't been able to drink at breakfast.

'Can I bring it back and drink it here?' Emma asked.

'Of course you can!' Susan answered composedly, trying to restrain any grimaces or groans. 'Don't worry about me, Emma, I'm really tough.'

'I thought you were going to die!' Emma swung round to cry.

Her expression reached Susan's heart, but she couldn't handle an over-emotional situation. 'You don't die from a bump on the head, darling, just get knocked out. Get your milk and hurry back.'

She wasn't gone a moment before Felicia came to the open door, offering no sympathy. 'I think you must be the most accident-prone girl I've ever met in my life.'

'Sure to be,' Susan sighed. 'Would I sound rude if I asked you to go? You've said your bit and just look at me.'

'There's a good possibility you did it on purpose!' Felicia's dark eyes were hooded and cold.

'Too painful!' Susan quavered, too amused to be outraged.

'Then how does it feel having Dev dancing attention on you?' Felicia demanded with a look of cold fury. Her thin nostrils were flaring and there were shadows under her eyes as if she had slept badly.

'Please leave me alone.' Susan half lifted her head. 'I'm sorry if you have to wait a bit longer for me to be gone.'

'I mean, hell, what does he *see* in you?' Felicia advanced on the bed for all the world as if she was going to hammer Susan with blows. 'I suppose you know he had to destroy a valuable horse?'

'Oh, *no*!' Susan closed her eyes with a momentary flash of severe pain. 'Not poor little Silky. I loved her.'

'Yes, Silky!' Felicia said harshly. 'You terrified the poor thing beyond all endurance. She crashed into a fence and had to be put down.'

'Oh, no!' Susan was moaning, her hand pressed against her mouth. 'He didn't tell me.'

'He didn't like to hound you,' Felicia said relentlessly, 'but I know damned well what he felt. He loves his horses and Silky was probably his best little mare. I told him at the time it wasn't a good thing to let you ride her. Now look what's happened. He's lost a valuable horse.'

'Go away!' Weak tears were sliding down Susan's face, and she turned her head away, breathing harshly, while she struggled for a breath without pain. That lovely little horse destroyed! Silky of the soft, starry eyes and the patrician head. Silky who always met her with a welcoming whinny, thrusting her head eagerly over the fence. Delicate head, large lustrous eyes, very feminine, dainty and affectionate. Silky, who was no more. The news hit her like a great blow, far worse than her own injuries.

There was shouting in the room, but she scarcely heard it. Weakness and sedation were abandoning her to her grief. Emma was there, raging at her mother, Jeff. He had his hand on her shoulder. Then there was quiet. She still had her head buried, crying, when Devin turned her to face him.

'I want you to stop that,' he said commandingly, 'it won't help. You'll miss Silky, we both will. But damn it, you're here. I'm just not going to allow you to cry any more. You're only doing damage to yourself and it won't change anything. Life isn't simple. I've had to destroy beautiful animals before. Felicia should never have told you, only she's inflamed with jealousy. I should have realised before now.'

'I don't think I can bear it,' she answered miserably. 'That innocent little creature!'

'You must learn how to protect yourself.' Gently he stroked her hair away from her face. 'Learn how to handle danger and tragedy. It's our way of life.'

'No, I've got no business here!' She fought back the tears, her small face despairing. 'Felicia is right.'

Gradually she quietened, though she looked as heartbroken as a child. Jeff was allowed in to see her, a veil ripped from his eyes. Felicia Chandler was a murderous bitch in her rage and his sister's white, bruised face with its burning blue-violet eyes left him savagely angry. Only a sadist could have attacked her when she was looking so small and battered. The whole incident had cleared his vision in an instant and he had almost cheered the frantically yelling child. Felicia was every bit as 'nasty' as her small daughter called her.

Jess called in on her throughout the day, looking faintly stunned, but she heard no doors slamming or voices raised in violence. It wasn't until she was allowed up days later after Dr Grant's visit that Emma told her her mother had flown out, leaving her daughter behind.

'But for how long?' Susan looked as bewildered as she felt.

'For ever!' Emma's calm voice matched her eyes. 'I heard her shouting that she was never coming back.'

'How dreadful!' Blindly Susan reached out to take the child's hand.

'She never wanted me, you know!' Emma explained composedly. 'I'm an encumbrance.'

'Emma, Emma,' Susan said over and over, as clearly as a prayer. She was struggling to accept that Felicia could possibly abandon her daughter. How could any mother do that?

Jess gave her more details, evidently considering Susan had to know. 'Lord grant that little child gets some peace and stability now.' She reached over and switched on the kettle to make tea. 'Mrs Chandler left days ago, still screaming hysterically. She lost out on the greatest prize of her life, and she was never a good loser.'

'I would have thought Emma was that,' Susan said quietly. 'How do you imagine that poor child feels?'

'You've seen her,' Jess pointed out matter-of-factly. 'It's the sad truth that Mrs Chandler made no attempt to reach her little daughter. She found the child a disappointment and she didn't always manage to hide the fact. Now she considers Mr Chandler should rear his niece. He's her legal guardian and he'll be handling the child's money until she comes of age. Not that Mrs Chandler lost out financially. Just between the two of us, I think it was part of the deal. I know Mr Chandler has been worried about Emma for a long while now. For all her coldness, Mrs Chandler is an uncontrolled kind of woman. Still, she wouldn't be able to manage long without Mr Chandler's support. Until she remarries, that is. Any decent man would have to run for his life, but she has other qualities that get them in.'

Susan was unaware that she was squeezing her hands

together so tightly, Jess had to reach over and touch her. 'Don't fret, love. Everything will come right in the end. Now, I've made a cake specially and I expect you to eat it. I can see all your bones.'

At this point Emma, in red shorts and a torn T-shirt, whirled through the kitchen door.

'Hi, just in time!' She flashed a smile at both women, reached out to pull the chocolate cake further towards her, then sat down companionably at the table. 'That looks scrumptious, Mrs Hansen.'

'Aye, it is!' Jess nodded her head in entire agreement. Wasn't her cooking famous, and rightly so?

Susan smiled, seeing something in Emma's face she had never noticed before. A quiet confidence, a certainty, that sat well on her plain little dignified face. Emma, in the right hands, would develop very quickly. It twisted Susan's heart to think she had to say goodbye to her.

CHAPTER EIGHT

THERE seemed no time to discuss her plans for leaving. After days of rain every creek, every waterhole, every lagoon on the property from boundary to boundary was running a banker. To everyone's immense relief cyclone Anna had crossed the coast north of Cooktown where it would do the least damage and spent itself in the jungle, scarring the canopy of the rain forest. Jeff was isolated at the outstation and the men were kept busy cleaning up the swirling tangle of debris and keeping the young calves from drowning. Green grass came up everywhere right through the foaming water and the whole landscape was an incredibly lush profusion of greenery and great sheets of silvery water.

Dev left the house in the morning and never came back all day. When he did, he greeted his niece warmly, told her as much as he thought advisable about what was happening on the property, then sank rather wearily into a planter's chair while Jess hurried up eagerly with a stiff drink. That same day one of the men had put his horse into a flood and got swept a mile downstream with the terrified horse trying to rear out of the water instead of swimming. Eventually Dev had had to ride his own horse into the swiftly flowing current while the stockman jumped clear and fastened on to the boss's big gelding's tail. Then with the stockman safely ashore, Dev had had to go back for the horse, that was trying to drown itself mid-stream through sheer terror. Eventually he managed to calm it to the extent that it followed the big bay gelding's example and swam back to the bank where it spewed out a good deal of water. Most of Lara's horses were good swimmers, but there was always the odd one that panicked in fast running water.

Emma listened fascinated to everything and her presence certainly reduced the faint tension at the dinner table, but Susan knew she couldn't persist with the impossible. She was afraid to face Dev, yet she knew she had to.

When Emma had gone to bed and Dev was working in his study, with no need of anyone outside himself, she tapped on the door with a trembling hand and waited for his autocratic: 'Come in.'

He was seated behind the great Victorian mahogany desk, his head lifted, his striking dark face without a smile. He was so many people, she had found out; now he wore the aloof formidability that frightened her,

'May I speak to you?' Her voice sounded nervous and rather hushed.

'I've been expecting it!' He stood up without taking his eyes off her, came round the desk and gently propelled her into a black leather armchair, swivelling it until she faced him. 'Here, take the weight off your trembling legs.'

'Thanks.' She didn't sink into it, but sat up straight, looking very fragile and feminine in that emphatically male room with its guns and its trophies and its collection of native artifacts.

'You're looking a lot better!' he pointed out rather curtly, then glanced at her blue dress. It was simple and inexpensive, but the tiny bodice clung to her and the skirt ruffled around her like a flower deepening the colour of her eyes. 'Well, what is it?' he prompted. 'I've a feeling you've judged the time ripe for a heart to heart chat.'

'No, Dev,' she corrected quietly, 'I've made my decision.'

'At some torment,' he said dryly, and leant back negligently against the carved desk, obviously waiting for her to go on.

She sighed deeply, finished examing her hands, then looked up at him with an exhausted air. 'I can't stay here as if I've got nowhere else to go. As soon as you have the time could you arrange a flight out for me to the coast? I did have a teaching career and it's about time I got on with it.'

'When do you think would be the right time?' he enquired in that same dry mocking tone.

'Well, the weather's not going to get any better,' she said, feeling harassed by his cruelty.

He agreed. 'Not with another cyclone coming at us from Fiji.'

'*Please*, Dev!' She stood up in her agitation, almost ecstatically wringing her hands. 'I'll be sad to leave Emma, and I think she'll miss me, but she's so much happier and stable these days. I hate to say it, but her mother was hurting her and you've given her security. I don't think you should send her to boarding school for at least another year. Hire a governess. There are plenty of young teachers who would be glad of the job.'

'Not you?' His green eyes pinned her, brilliant and pitiless.

'No.' She knew she sounded like a little girl trying not to cry. 'I'm leaving.'

'Just a little scared redhead?'

'I suppose so. I'm sorry, Dev.'

'Who for?' He reached out and tilted her drooping head. 'Emma? Yourself?'

'Not you. You're no ordinary man.'

'So they tell me, and I don't always want to hear it.'

She felt the flick of his anger and flushed, her hair falling loosely in a riot of deep waves and curls. 'If it would be any help to you I could try to find a suitable governess for Emma.'

'That's all right!' He dismissed her suggestion crisply. 'My solicitors will handle it or one of the pastoral companies. I'm never short of help.'

'Well then,' she tilted her chin with delicate dignity, 'thank you for everything; the most incredible experience of my life.'

'Have you got money?' His voice sounded quite hard and businesslike.

'And don't dare offer me any!' She was bristling with indignation and a monumental despair. 'I want nothing from you ... nothing!' She clenched her fists and held them high and he swooped her up and carried her back to the long leather sofa, holding her across his knees.

'It's time you and I came to an understanding,' he snapped. 'You told me once you loved me, now I want to hear it again.'

'Not ever!'

'Just a minute.' He pulled her right up into his arms, shaping her shoulder and keeping on.

'I'll scream, Dev,' she promised him, sounding foolish and frightened even to herself.

'Go ahead, scream.'

'Please!' She had her eyes closed against the invading sensations.

'But I want to. You've no idea how much.'

She knew it would happen, still she didn't open her eyes. His mouth was moving over hers slowly, teasing her, testing, going back and forth over her full, sensitive lips, shocking her with pleasure, so that when she went to reach out involuntarily to touch him he held her hands deliberately at her side, continuing to kiss her until she wanted to scream.

'*Dev!*' Her little moan was frantic.

'Tell me. Go ahead and I'll let you go.'

'I can't.'

'*Now!*' Kisses, caresses. She was nearly delirious.

'I love you.' He had it out of her, and immediately he released her hands.

'Thank you. Nothing would ever make sense again if you hadn't said that.'

Her trembling subsided and her eyes flew open, the tears beginning to shimmer as she looked on his face. He had never looked at her before with such naked emotion: the possessiveness, the tenderness, the lover's brilliant sensuality for the loved one. The one woman. It was incredible, and a wild elation began to fill her.

'You didn't really think I was going to let you go?' he asked quietly. 'You're mine, Susan. Mine alone. Believe it.'

'And I accept it gladly!' she cried. 'But don't you see I'm begging you to love me as well as want me? I'll stay with you for ever, but you must let me into your heart. I couldn't bear it if you shut me out. I have such a truly dreadful need of you.'

'That makes two of us!' His mouth twisted slightly,

with self-mockery and charm. 'You should know by now that you're absolutely essential to my peace of body and mind. Don't you know what you see? I love you. You're a joy. Just one fragile, lotus-eyed girl. I can handle a lot of things, but I can't handle my feelings for you. They go too deep and they're for ever. Till death do us part!' He bent his head and kissed her mouth hard. 'Are you strong enough?'

'Are you?' she challenged him.

'I love you, Susan.' His dark face was serious yet exultant. 'I'm determined to make you happy, but don't ever try to leave me. God help you if you do.'

'But how could I ever want to?' she blazed at him, delicate but strong. 'Don't you know me? You're perfect to me, beautiful, the ideal. I want our children. I'm going to love them so much. Can't you see how confident I am? I'm nothing without you. I'm even at home in your paradise with all the forces of nature raging.'

He laughed and hugged her to him. 'You haven't seen a cyclone yet.'

'I'll survive. *We'll* survive.' She put the palm of his hand to her mouth and kissed it. 'Give me my chance, Dev. That's all I ask—the privilege of being your wife.'

The strong hand that cupped her face, incredibly, trembled and he turned her until she was lying full length in his arms.

'Susan,' he said huskily. 'Susan. . . .'

Harlequin Romances

The books that let you escape
into the wonderful world of romance!
Trips to exotic places...interesting
plots...meeting memorable people...
the excitement of love....These are
integral parts of Harlequin Romances –
the heartwarming novels read by
women everywhere.

Many early issues are now available.
Choose from this great selection!

Choose from this list of classic Harlequin Romance editions.

Relive a great love story...
Harlequin Romances 1980
Complete and mail this coupon today!

Harlequin Reader Service

In U.S.A.
MPO Box 707
Niagara Falls, N.Y. 14302

In Canada
649 Ontario St.
Stratford, Ontario, N5A 6W2

Please send me the following Harlequin Romance novels. I am enclosing my check or money order for $1.25 for each novel ordered, plus 59¢ to cover postage and handling.

☐ 449	☐ 528	☐ 658	☐ 804	☐ 904	☐ 451
☐ 454	☐ 532	☐ 711	☐ 805	☐ 911	☐ 462
☐ 464	☐ 538	☐ 712	☐ 856	☐ 918	☐ 468
☐ 469	☐ 557	☐ 730	☐ 861	☐ 409	☐ 478
☐ 494	☐ 597	☐ 766	☐ 890	☐ 430	☐ 485
☐ 500	☐ 604	☐ 796	☐ 892	☐ 438	☐ 489
☐ 513	☐ 627	☐ 800	☐ 895	☐ 443	☐ 491
☐ 516	☐ 643	☐ 802	☐ 901	☐ 446	☐ 495

Number of novels checked @ $1.25 each = $_____

N.Y. State residents add appropriate sales tax $_____

Postage and handling $_____.59

TOTAL $_____

I enclose _____
(Please send check or money order. We cannot be responsible for cash sent through the mail.)

NAME _____
(Please Print)

ADDRESS _____

CITY _____

STATE/PROV. _____

ZIP/POSTAL CODE _____

Offer expires September 30, 1980.   00456426100

What readers say about Harlequin Romances

"Your books turn my…life into something quite exciting."
B.M.* Baldwin Park, California

"I have never read a Harlequin that I did not like. They are all wonderful books."
M.H., Hatboro, Pennsylvania

"Harlequin books have afforded me more pleasure than I ever anticipated."
C.S.P., Riverdale, Georgia

"I have one complaint…there are never enough Harlequins."
N.S., Horace, North Dakota

*Names available on request